Ikenaga 2 Jos Leys

"A relatively simple formula can generate immensely complex images." – Jos Leys

Investigations

IN NUMBER, DATA, AND SPACE®

Glenview, Illinois • Boston, Massachusetts
Chandler, Arizona • Upper Saddle River, New Jersey

The Investigations curriculum was developed by TERC, Cambridge, MA.

This material is based on work supported by the National Science Foundation ("NSF") under Grant No.ESI-0095450. Any opinions, findings, and conclusions or recommendations expressed in this material are those of the author(s) and do not necessarily reflect the views of the National Science Foundation.

ISBN-13: 978-0-328-62340-2

ISBN-10: 0-328-62340-7

5 6 7 8 9 10 V063 14 13 12

Contents

About This Guide

Overview

The *Differentiation and Intervention Guide* is a flexible and versatile component that supplements the *Investigations* curriculum units. An Intervention, Practice, and Extension activity is provided for every Investigation. The differentiation activities presented in this guide can be used anytime after the session referenced, such as during Math Workshops, or outside of math time. In addition, a Quiz is available to use as a formative assessment after an Investigation is completed.

Teachers may also assign multiple activities for an Investigation to a single student. For example, after a student completes the Practice activity, it may be appropriate for that student to work on the Extension activity. Similarly, Practice and Extension activities can also be used to reinforce and extend Intervention suggestions, either during the Investigation or later in the unit.

Within each curriculum unit, a feature titled "Differentiation: Supporting the Range of Learners" appears regularly. This feature offers ideas for Intervention, Extension, and ELL related to the content of that session. The *Differentiation and Intervention Guide* expands many of these existing Intervention and Extension suggestions by providing teaching suggestions and/or student masters. The *Differentiation and Intervention Guide* also provides additional Practice activities for all students.

Curriculum Unit 2, p. 18

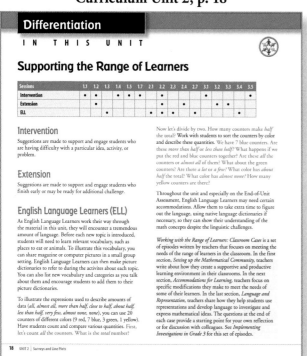

Differentiation suggestions are embedded in the curriculum units.

Curriculum Unit 2, p. 38

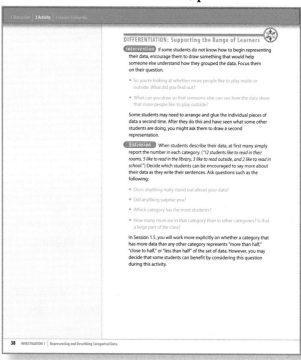

The Differentiation and Intervention Guide *enhances the existing differentiation suggestions in the curriculum units.*

Understanding This Guide

The *Differentiation and Intervention Guide* contains support pages for every Investigation in the curriculum units. The first page provides teachers with an overview of the key mathematics in the Investigation and descriptions of student performance. The remaining three pages provide easy-to-use activities based on the Math Focus Points in the Investigation. Each activity features built-in ELL support and resource masters for students.

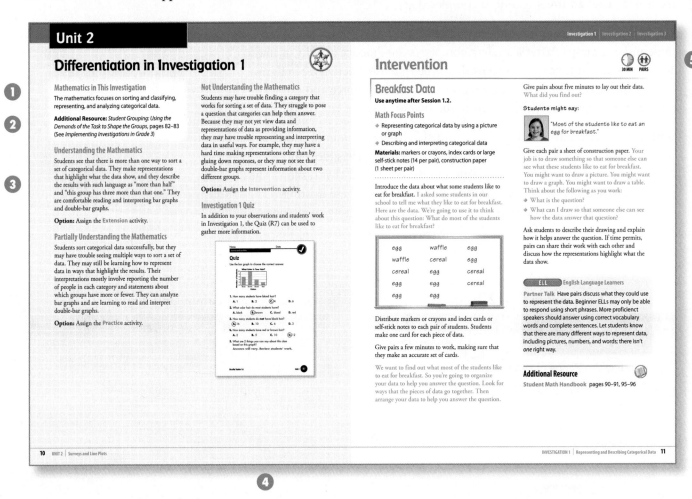

1 **Mathematics in This Investigation** gives an overview of the important mathematical ideas and skills students encounter during the Investigation.

2 **Additional Resources** provide teachers with information about pertinent Teacher Notes and/or Classroom Cases.

3 **Performance descriptions** assist teachers in determining differentiation activities based on observations of students throughout the Investigation and analyzing students' work.

4 The **Quiz** consists of 4 multiple-choice questions and 1 performance-based question. It can be used as an additional tool to help teachers identify students' levels of understanding of the mathematics in each Investigation.

5 Each differentiation activity is designed to be covered in 15 to 30 minutes in small groups, pairs, or as individuals.

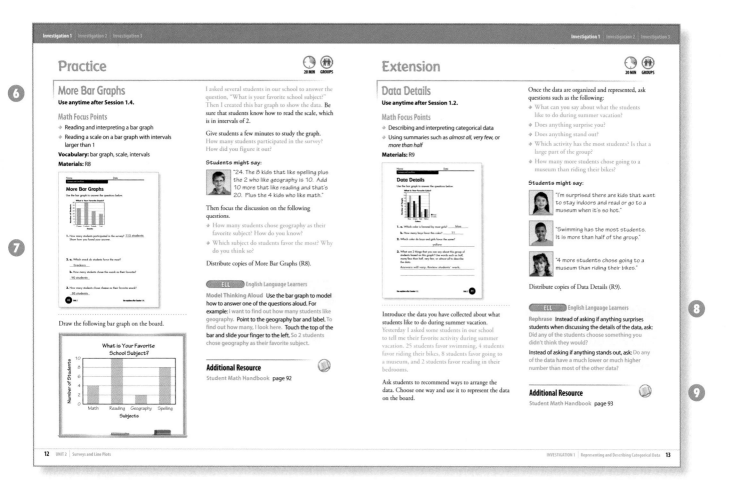

6 Activities can be used anytime after the session content is covered giving increased flexibility to teachers.

7 **Resource Masters** provide additional practice or are used as a recording sheet.

8 **ELL notes** provide teachers with suggestions to support students with language and vocabulary.

9 **Additional Resources** for students provide useful Student Math Handbook references or games to play for extra practice.

Supporting ELL Students

English Language Learners in the Math Classroom

Dr. Jim Cummins
University of Toronto

Research studies have demonstrated that English Language Learners (ELLs) generally pick up everyday conversational fluency within a year or two of starting to learn English. However, a much longer period (generally at least five years) is required for students to fully catch up to native speakers in academic language proficiency (e.g., vocabulary knowledge, reading and writing skills). In mathematics, ELL students often make good progress in acquiring basic computation skills in the early grades; however, they typically experience greater difficulty in carrying out word problems particularly as these problems become more complex linguistically in later grades.

Thus, ELL students are likely to require explicit *language* support within the classroom in order to achieve content standards in subject areas such as mathematics. Despite the fact that they have acquired conversational fluency in English together with basic mathematical vocabulary and computational skills, students may still experience gaps in their knowledge of more sophisticated vocabulary, syntax, and discourse features of mathematical language.

The linguistic challenges faced by ELL students in learning math reflect the fact that language is central to the teaching of virtually every school subject. The concepts embedded in the curriculum are inseparable from the language we use to teach these concepts to our students. For example, most mathematical problems require students to understand prepositions and logical relations that are expressed through language.

This fusion of language and content across the curriculum presents both challenges and opportunities in teaching ELL students. The challenges are to provide the instructional supports to enable ELL students to understand math content and carry out math tasks and operations. However, math instruction also provides teachers with the opportunity to extend ELL students' knowledge of language in ways that will significantly benefit their overall academic development. For example, as they learn mathematics, students are also learning that there are predictable patterns in how we form the abstract nouns that describe mathematical operations. Many of these nouns are formed by adding the suffix *–tion* to the verb, as in *add/addition, subtract/subtraction, multiply/multiplication,* etc. This knowledge can then be applied in other subject areas across the curriculum (e.g., science, language arts).

In building ELL supports for *Investigations*, we have been guided by *The Pearson ELL Curriculum Framework*, which incorporates the following five instructional principles central to teaching ELL students effectively.

1. Identify and Communicate Content and Language Objectives In planning and organizing a lesson, teachers must first identify what content and language objectives they want to communicate to students. The language objectives might include providing definitions, descriptions, examples, and visual supports for explaining vocabulary.

2. Frontload the Lesson Frontloading refers to the use of prereading or preinstructional strategies that prepare ELL students to understand new academic content. Frontloading strategies include activating prior knowledge, building background, previewing text, preteaching vocabulary, and making connections.

3. Provide Comprehensible Input Language and content that students can understand is referred to as comprehensible input. Teachers make use of nonlinguistic supports to enable students to understand language and content that would otherwise have been beyond their comprehension. Typical supports include visuals, models, and manipulatives.

4. Enable Language Production Language production complements comprehensible input and is an essential element in developing expertise in academic language. Use of both oral and written language enables students to solve problems, generate insights, express their ideas, and obtain feedback from teachers and peers.

5. Assess for Content and Language Understanding Finally, the instructional cycle flows into assessing what students have learned and then spirals upward into further development of students' content knowledge and language expertise.

These principles come to life in the *Differentiation and Intervention Guide* in the form of seven specific instructional strategies.

- *Model Thinking Aloud* When ELL students articulate their thinking processes through language, they are enabled to complete activities, identify gaps in their knowledge, and receive feedback from teachers. Teachers, however, must model this process in order for students to learn how to use it effectively. When modeling thinking aloud, it is important for teachers to use visuals and gestures.

- *Partner Talk* When it comes to working on a math activity of any kind, two heads are often better than one. Partner talk provides an audience for students' thinking aloud and an opportunity for the teacher to direct students to listen for particular vocabulary and linguistic structures as they engage in a task with their partner.

- *Provide a Word List* When students make a list of relevant vocabulary in a lesson with examples of how these words are used, it reinforces their knowledge of this vocabulary and provides an opportunity for teachers to monitor their understanding and provide additional explanation as needed. Paying special attention to homophones, such as *sum* and *some*, is particularly helpful for ELL students.

- *Provide Sentence Stems* Sentence stems provide support for ELL students to gain access to the sequence of steps in an activity, and they expand students' knowledge of how to communicate their thinking processes to the teacher and their peers.

- *Rephrase* Students struggling with vocabulary and language acquisition are often confused by extra details in word problems or overly wordy statements. Rephrasing statements in a different way that utilizes simpler language, shorter sentences, and eliminates unnecessary information helps students focus on and understand the important information needed to work through an activity.

- *Suggest a Sequence* Sequencing of steps is crucial to solving many math problems, and ELL students may need additional help in this process. Providing struggling ELL students with a sequence of steps to follow provides them with a guide for how to complete an activity or report their findings. When suggesting a sequence, be sure to use concise language.

- *Use Repetition* Repetition of instructions or explanations may also be required to enable ELL students to fully understand instruction. Because students are still in the process of learning English, they may need repetition, paraphrasing, or elaboration to understand teacher talk containing new vocabulary or structures.

Differentiation in Investigation 1

Mathematics in This Investigation

The mathematics focuses on place value, on using 100s, 10s, and 1s to represent numbers, and on adding 10 and multiples of 10 to, and subtracting them from, 2-digit numbers.

Understanding the Mathematics

Students know the total when shown a number of 10s and 1s, and can use 10s and 1s to represent a given amount. They are similarly fluent with money. When asked to find combinations of 10s and 1s that make a given number, they see and use relationships between combinations to generate all or most of the combinations. They often "just know" the answer when 10 is added to or subtracted from a number, and they can add and subtract multiples of 10 fluently.

Option: Assign the Extension activity.

Partially Understanding the Mathematics

Students figure out the total when shown a number of 10s and 1s, and can use 10s and 1s to represent a given amount. They name and identify coins and know the coin values, but may not yet count or work with combinations of coins fluently. They can find many combinations of 10s and 1s that make a given number, but are just beginning to see and use relationships between combinations. They may solve problems that involve adding or subtracting 10 and multiples of 10 by modeling them with cubes, stickers, or 100 charts.

Option: Assign the Practice activity.

Not Understanding the Mathematics

Students may have to count in part by 1s to figure out the total when shown a number of 10s and 1s, or to figure out how to use 10s and 1s to represent a given amount. They may not be fluent with the values of the coins, and counting or working with combinations of coins is likely a challenge. They may find only one combination of 10s and 1s that makes a given number (e.g., 3 tens and 7 ones for 37), and be unaware that other combinations exist. They may count on or back by 1s to solve problems that involve adding or subtracting 10 and multiples of 10.

Option: Assign the Intervention activity.

Investigation 1 Quiz

In addition to your observations and students' work in Investigation 1, the Quiz (R1) can be used to gather more information.

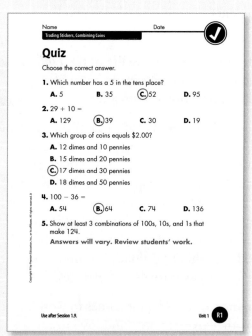

Intervention

25 MIN **PAIRS**

Adding 2-Digit Numbers

Use anytime after Session 1.2.

Math Focus Points

◆ Recognizing and representing the place value of each digit in 2- and 3-digit numbers

◆ Adding and subtracting multiples of 10

Vocabulary: tens place, ones place, equation

Materials: cubes in towers of 10 (5 of one color, 1 of another color per pair)

. . . .

Adapt the situation in Adding and Subtracting 10s and 1s (page 40) as follows. Maria has 35 stickers. She went to Sticker Station and bought one more strip of 10 stickers. How many stickers does Maria have now?

How many stickers did Maria start with? Encourage students to use cubes to model the starting amount. How many towers of 10 did you use? How many single cubes did you use?

Then, Maria bought one more strip of 10 stickers. Ask students to use cubes of another color to model the new amount.

Reread the problem and ask students what they are trying to figure out. How can we find out how many stickers Maria has now?

As you discuss students' strategies, focus on the groups of 10. Count by 10s together to reinforce that 4 groups of 10 equals 40. Then count on by 1s together to get a total of 45.

Ask students to help you write an equation for this problem on the board. Emphasize the vocabulary and meaning of words like *plus*, *equals*, and *sum*.

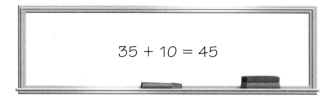

$$35 + 10 = 45$$

Now Maria has 45 stickers. Suppose that she went back to Sticker Station and bought one more strip of 10 stickers. Now how many stickers does she have? Encourage students to model and solve the problem, and to write an equation for it. Record $45 + 10 = 55$ under the first equation.

Finally, record the numbers 35, 45, and 55 in a column on the board. What do you notice about these numbers? What's changing and what's staying the same?

ELL English Language Learners

Model Thinking Aloud Model thinking aloud and then ask volunteers to do the same. Listen for complete sentences and the correct use of vocabulary.

Maria started with 35 stickers so I took 35 blue cubes. Then, Maria got 10 more stickers so I took 10 red cubes. To count them, I grouped the tens and the ones. Model counting by 10s and then counting on by 1s for students who need support with this kind of counting in English.

Additional Resource

Student Math Handbook page 12

Practice

20 MIN **PAIRS**

Practicing Adding and Subtracting 10s

Use anytime after Session 1.2.

Math Focus Points

◆ Adding and subtracting multiples of 10

Vocabulary: equation

Materials: 100 cubes in towers of 10, class pocket 100 chart, M4, R2

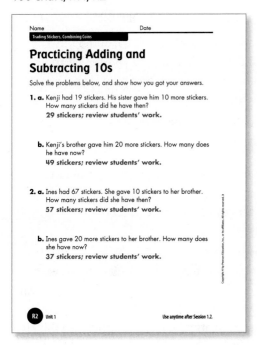

Read the following problem aloud. Jane had 52 stickers. Her brother gave her 10 more. How many stickers did she have then?

Give students time to find the solution using sketches of stickers, cubes, or the 100 chart (M4) as needed. Then ask for volunteers to explain their solutions. How did you determine the total number of stickers?

Students might say:

 "Jane started with 52 stickers, so I found 52 on the 100 chart. She got 10 more, so I went down one row to 62."

 "If I had 52 cubes I'd have to add one more tower of 10 and that would give me 53, 54, 55, 56, 57, 58, 59, 60, 61, 62."

Ask students for an equation for this problem and record 52 + 10 = 62 on the board.

Now Jane has 62 stickers. If she uses 20 stickers, how many stickers will she have left?

Give students a few minutes to work and then ask volunteers to explain their solutions. Use cubes, sketches, and the class pocket 100 chart to compare students' strategies. As students respond, write the second equation on the board underneath the first one.

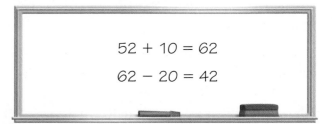

$$52 + 10 = 62$$
$$62 - 20 = 42$$

Distribute copies of Practicing Adding and Subtracting 10s (R2).

ELL English Language Learners

Partner Talk Have students explain the parts of each equation to a partner. Encourage more proficient speakers to use words such as *more, add, sum, less, subtract, difference,* and *equation.* Less proficient speakers can point to the parts of the equations as they explain.

Additional Resource

Student Math Handbook page 36

Extension

20 MIN PAIRS

More Sticker Combinations

Use anytime after Session 1.8.

Math Focus Points

◆ Recognizing and representing the place value of each digit in 2- and 3-digit numbers

◆ Recognizing and demonstrating the equivalence of one 100 to ten 10s and of one 10 to ten 1s

Materials: *Student Activity Book* p. 31 (from Session 1.8), R3

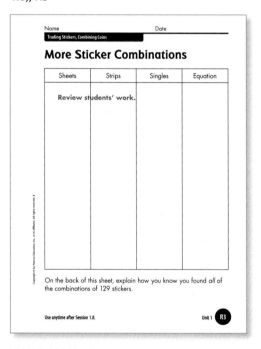

Remind students of their discussion in Session 1.8 about their work on finding combinations that made 137 stickers.

We found many different combinations of hundreds, tens, and ones for 137 stickers. Your challenge today is to find all of the different combinations of hundreds, tens, and ones for 137 stickers, and to prove that you've found them all.

Students work in pairs to find all of the combinations. They record their work on *Student Activity Book* page 31. Give them time to complete the activity and then discuss their work.

How many combinations of 137 did you find? Once you agree that there are 18 combinations, focus on students' reasoning about how they know they have them all. *How do you know there are 18 combinations? How do you know there aren't any others we've missed?*

Students might say:

"First I did all the ways I could that had 1 sheet of stickers. Then I found all the ways that just use strips and singles. And then there will always be one that's all singles."

End by asking students to think about another 3-digit number. *How many combinations do you think there are for 129? Do you think there will be more or less than there were for 137?*

Students might say:

"I think there will be less. It's a smaller number."

Distribute copies of More Sticker Combinations (R3) for students to use to list all of the combinations.

ELL English Language Learners

Partner Talk Have more proficient speakers explain what makes up a combination in the chart as the other partner points to the row that represents that combination. Model for students how to use words such as *hundreds*, *tens*, *ones*, and *equals* in their explanations.

Additional Resource

Student Math Handbook page 9

Differentiation in Investigation 2

Mathematics in This Investigation

The mathematics focuses on finding combinations of numbers whose total is as close as possible to 100, and finding the difference between 2- and 3-digit numbers and 100.

Additional Resources: *Learning the Addition Combinations,* pages 159–160 (See Curriculum Unit 1); *The Case of Ezra Who "Just Knows" the Answer,* pages 86–87 (See *Implementing Investigations in Grade 3*)

Understanding the Mathematics

Students make two 2-digit numbers whose sum is as close as possible to 100 using estimation, knowledge of place value, and fluency with pairs of numbers that add up to 10 or 100. They are similarly comfortable with combinations of coins that make a dollar. They combine 2-digit numbers and can efficiently find the difference between the sum and 100. They are fluent with the addition combinations to 10 + 10.

Option: Assign the Extension activity.

Partially Understanding the Mathematics

Students make two 2-digit numbers whose sum is close to 100, but may not realize that there are combinations that land exactly on, or get closer to, 100. They are becoming more comfortable finding the total of a group of coins, but are not yet fluent. They may total the amount on each, or most, of eight Coin Cards, and then consider which combination of cards add up to $1.00. Most students count up to find the difference between 100 and 2-digit or small 3-digit numbers. They are fluent with most of the addition combinations to 10 + 10, but continue to use strategies for a few of them (e.g., counting on, using a related fact they know).

Option: Assign the Practice activity.

Not Understanding the Mathematics

When asked to make two 2-digit numbers with a sum as close as possible to 100, students may work somewhat randomly. They record sums without considering other possibilities and whether other sums would land them closer to 100. Their strategies do not seem to rely on knowledge of place value (e.g., the number of 10s in both numbers), estimation (e.g., a number in the 60s needs a number in the 30s or 40s to go with it), or facts they know (e.g., 7 + 3 = 10 so 70 + 30 = 100). Finding the total of a group of coins is challenging, as is finding combinations of coins that make a dollar. Students may model the problem or count by 1s to find the difference between 100 and 2-digit or small 3-digit numbers. They are fluent with some of the addition combinations to 10 + 10, but they continue to use strategies for many of them (e.g., counting on, using a related fact they know).

Option: Assign the Intervention activity.

Investigation 2 Quiz

In addition to your observations and students' work in Investigation 2, the Quiz (R4) can be used to gather more information.

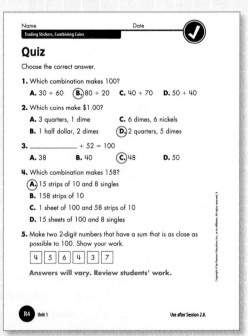

Intervention

20 MIN   PAIRS

Practicing Finding Sums That Equal 100

Use anytime after Session 2.3.

Math Focus Points

◆ Using knowledge of place value to find pairs of 2-digit numbers that add to 100 or a number close to 100

◆ Using known pairs of 2-digit numbers that add to 100 to find related pairs that add to 100 or a number close to 100 (for example, 20 + 80 = 100, so 22 + 78 = 100)

Materials: "Ways to Make 100" chart (from Session 2.2, p. 103), cubes in towers of 10 (10 per pair)

. . . .

Distribute cubes to each pair of students. Begin the activity by reviewing the "Ways to Make 100" chart that you made together in Session 2.2 (page 103). Review the relationship between the make-10 combinations and the make-100 combinations. Write the following equation on the board.

$$40 + \underline{\qquad} = 100$$

What make-10 combination can you use to help you figure out what to add to 40 to make 100?

Students might say:

"4 + 6 = 10."

Record the combination of 10 on the board. Work with your partner. Think about how knowing that 4 + 6 = 10 can help you. Use cubes to show your answer.

$$4 + 6 = 10$$
$$40 + \underline{\qquad} = 100$$

Ask a pair of students to show how they used cubes to find what they needed to add to 40 to make 100. Repeat the above with a similar problem: $70 + \underline{\quad} = 100$. So far we've found ways to make 100 by adding multiples of 10. Now let's find two numbers that are *not* multiples of 10 that make 100.

$$7 + \underline{3} = 10$$
$$70 + \underline{30} = 100$$
$$71 + \underline{\quad} = 100$$

Students use cubes to model and solve the problem. Record the solutions on the board.

ELL English Language Learners

Rephrase Go over the activity again, rephrasing the main ideas. I used a make-10 combination to help me find multiples of 10 that have a sum of 100. Then I used the multiples of 10 to help me make two numbers that *do not have a zero in the ones place* that add to 100.

Additional Resource

Student Math Handbook pages 13–15

Practice

20 MIN   PAIRS

Making Sums Close to 100
Use anytime after Session 2.2.

Math Focus Points

◆ Using known pairs of 2-digit numbers that add to 100 to find related pairs that add to 100 or a number close to 100 (for example, 20 + 80 = 100, so 22 + 78 = 100)

Materials: Digit Cards (1 deck per pair), M36, R5

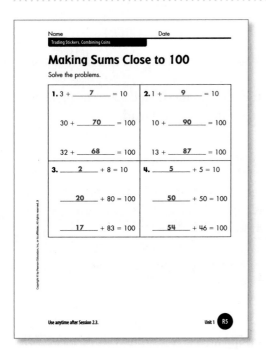

Review the rules for playing *Close to 100* and then play a sample round together. Suppose that these are the six cards you get. Place the following cards:

3	7	1	9	5	2

One strategy I've seen is thinking about what you know about 100. I'm going to make the number 25. Think about what you know about 100. What number would you need to add to get 100 exactly? Do we have a 7 and a 5? What could we do instead?

Work together to determine the sum of 25 and 73 and its distance from 100. So we found two 2-digit numbers that make 98. But maybe we could get even closer. What if I make the number 71? What multiple of 10 is that close to? What would you need to add to 70 to get exactly 100? Can we make a number that is close to 30 with our cards? Work together to find the sum of 71 and the numbers students suggest. Agree on an answer and model recording it and determining your score on the *Close to 100* Recording Sheet (M36). Remember, your score is the difference between your total and 100. Since 71 + [29] = 100, your score is [0].

Pick six new cards; 1, 5, 6, 4, 9, and 0. Think about the strategies we just discussed and what you know about 100. What do you see in these numbers that might help us solve this problem? Ask students to think and then talk to a partner about what they notice. Discuss several students' ideas. Once in agreement, students write the two numbers, their sum, and the score on their recording sheets. Students will play with a partner until the recording sheet is complete. Then distribute copies of Making Sums Close to 100 (R5).

 ELL **English Language Learners**

Model Thinking Aloud Help students understand how to make numbers that are close to 100 by reminding them to start with using known number combinations of 100. I know that 20 and 80 make 100. So I can start with the number 19 and make a number that is close to 80.

Additional Resource

Student Math Handbook
Game: *Close to 100* SMH G5
Materials: Digit Cards, M36

Extension

20 MIN **PAIRS**

The Dollar Store

Use anytime after Session 2.4.

Math Focus Points

◆ Finding combinations of coins that equal $1.00

◆ Recognizing and using coin equivalencies

Materials: coin and dollar sets (1 per pair), blank paper, R6

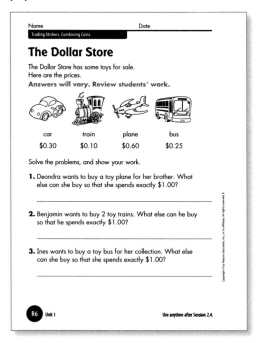

Students solve problems involving items for sale at The Dollar Store. Every purchase must total *exactly* one dollar. Write the following price list on the board.

pencil	$0.10
ruler	$0.25
marker	$0.40
paper clip	$0.05
envelope	$0.20

Explain that purchases may include more than one of any item. What would you buy? What coins would you pay with?

Students might say:

"I would buy 2 markers for 80¢ and then 1 envelope is 20¢ more so that's a dollar. I would pay with 4 quarters."

Discuss different combinations of items that total $1.00 exactly. List the combinations that students share as equations, sometimes using decimal notation and sometimes using the cent sign. Also list the coins used for the purchase. Explain that students can use any combination of coins to make a total of $1.00.

Then pairs work to generate and record different combinations of items that cost exactly $1.00, and the coins used to purchase them, on a piece of paper.

Distribute copies of The Dollar Store (R6).

> **ELL** English Language Learners

Model Thinking Aloud Model your thinking for making a purchase aloud. I wanted to spend exactly $1.00. I decided to buy 2 markers and 1 envelope. I know 1 marker costs 40¢, so 2 markers cost 80¢; 20¢ more for 1 envelope makes $1.00. I know that 4 quarters equal 1 dollar, so I decided to pay with 4 quarters.

Additional Resource

Student Math Handbook

Game: *Make a Dollar* SMH G16

Materials: Coin Cards, M43

Variation: Make combinations of cards that equal any whole number of dollars.

Differentiation in Investigation 1

Mathematics in This Investigation

The mathematics focuses on sorting and classifying, representing, and analyzing categorical data.

Additional Resource: *Student Grouping: Using the Demands of the Task to Shape the Groups*, pages 82–83 (See *Implementing Investigations in Grade 3*)

Understanding the Mathematics

Students see that there is more than one way to sort a set of categorical data. They make representations that highlight what the data show, and they describe the results with such language as "more than half" and "this group has three more than that one." They are comfortable reading and interpreting bar graphs and double-bar graphs.

Option: Assign the Extension activity.

Partially Understanding the Mathematics

Students sort categorical data successfully, but they may have trouble seeing multiple ways to sort a set of data. They may still be learning how to represent data in ways that highlight the results. Their interpretations mostly involve reporting the number of people in each category and statements about which groups have more or fewer. They can analyze bar graphs and are learning to read and interpret double-bar graphs.

Option: Assign the Practice activity.

Not Understanding the Mathematics

Students may have trouble finding a category that works for sorting a set of data. They struggle to pose a question that categories can help them answer. Because they may not yet view data and representations of data as providing information, they may have trouble representing and interpreting data in useful ways. For example, they may have a hard time making representations other than by gluing down responses, or they may not see that double-bar graphs represent information about two different groups.

Option: Assign the Intervention activity.

Investigation 1 Quiz

In addition to your observations and students' work in Investigation 1, the Quiz (R7) can be used to gather more information.

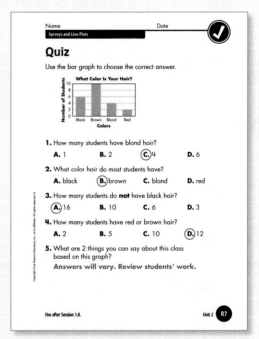

Intervention

30 MIN   PAIRS

Breakfast Data

Use anytime after Session 1.2.

Math Focus Points

◆ Representing categorical data by using a picture or graph

◆ Describing and interpreting categorical data

Materials: markers or crayons, index cards or large self-stick notes (14 per pair), construction paper (1 sheet per pair)

. . . .

Introduce the data about what some students like to eat for breakfast. *I asked some students in our school to tell me what they like to eat for breakfast. Here are the data. We're going to use it to think about this question: What do most of the students like to eat for breakfast?*

egg	waffle	egg
waffle	cereal	egg
cereal	egg	cereal
egg	egg	cereal
egg	egg	

Distribute markers or crayons and index cards or self-stick notes to each pair of students. Students make one card for each piece of data.

Give pairs a few minutes to work, making sure that they make an accurate set of cards.

We want to find out what most of the students like to eat for breakfast. So you're going to organize your data to help you answer the question. Look for ways that the pieces of data go together. Then arrange your data to help you answer the question.

Give pairs about five minutes to lay out their data. *What did you find out?*

Students might say:

"Most of the students like to eat an egg for breakfast."

Give each pair a sheet of construction paper. *Your job is to draw something so that someone else can see what these students like to eat for breakfast. You might want to draw a picture. You might want to draw a graph. You might want to draw a table. Think about the following as you work:*

◆ *What is the question?*

◆ *What can I draw so that someone else can see how the data answer that question?*

Ask students to describe their drawing and explain how it helps answer the question. If time permits, pairs can share their work with each other and discuss how the representations highlight what the data show.

━━━━━━━━━━━━━━━

ELL **English Language Learners**

Partner Talk Have pairs discuss what they could use to represent the data. Beginner ELLs may only be able to respond using short phrases. More proficienct speakers should answer using correct vocabulary words and complete sentences. Let students know that there are many different ways to represent data, including pictures, numbers, and words; there isn't *one* right way.

━━━━━━━━━━━━━━━

Additional Resource

Student Math Handbook pages 90–91, 95–96

Practice

20 MIN   GROUPS

More Bar Graphs

Use anytime after Session 1.4.

Math Focus Points

◆ Reading and interpreting a bar graph

◆ Reading a scale on a bar graph with intervals larger than 1

Vocabulary: bar graph, scale, intervals

Materials: R8

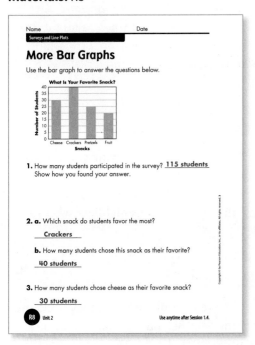

Draw the following bar graph on the board.

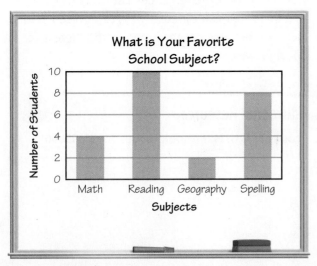

I asked several students in our school to answer the question, "What is your favorite school subject?" Then I created this bar graph to show the data. Be sure that students know how to read the scale, which is in intervals of 2.

Give students a few minutes to study the graph. How many students participated in the survey? How did you figure it out?

Students might say:

"24. The 8 kids that like spelling plus the 2 who like geography is 10. Add 10 more that like reading and that's 20. Plus the 4 kids who like math."

Then focus the discussion on the following questions.

◆ How many students chose geography as their favorite subject? How do you know?

◆ Which subject do students favor the most? Why do you think so?

Distribute copies of More Bar Graphs (R8).

ELL   English Language Learners

Model Thinking Aloud Use the bar graph to model how to answer one of the questions aloud. For example: I want to find out how many students like geography. Point to the geography bar and label. To find out how many, I look here. Touch the top of the bar and slide your finger to the left. So 2 students chose geography as their favorite subject.

Additional Resource

Student Math Handbook page 92

Extension

20 MIN   GROUPS

Data Details

Use anytime after Session 1.2.

Math Focus Points

◆ Describing and interpreting categorical data

◆ Using summaries such as *almost all, very few,* or *more than half*

Materials: R9

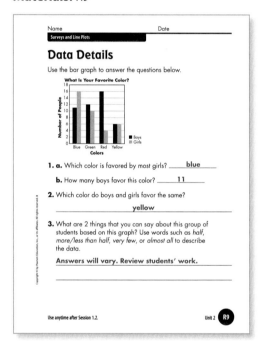

Introduce the data you have collected about what students like to do during summer vacation. Yesterday I asked some students in our school to tell me their favorite activity during summer vacation. 25 students favor swimming, 4 students favor riding their bikes, 8 students favor going to a museum, and 2 students favor reading in their bedrooms.

Ask students to recommend ways to arrange the data. Choose one way and use it to represent the data on the board.

Once the data are organized and represented, ask questions such as the following:

◆ What can you say about what the students like to do during summer vacation?

◆ Does anything surprise you?

◆ Does anything stand out?

◆ Which activity has the most students? Is that a large part of the group?

◆ How many more students chose going to a museum than riding their bikes?

Students might say:

"I'm surprised there are kids that want to stay indoors and read or go to a museum when it's so hot."

"Swimming has the most students. It is more than half of the group."

"4 more students chose going to a museum than riding their bikes."

Distribute copies of Data Details (R9).

ELL **English Language Learners**

Rephrase Instead of asking if anything surprises students when discussing the details of the data, ask: Did any of the students choose something you didn't think they would?

Instead of asking if anything stands out, ask: Do any of the data have a much lower or much higher number than most of the other data?

Additional Resource

Student Math Handbook page 93

Differentiation in Investigation 2

Mathematics in This Investigation

The mathematics focuses on collecting, representing, and interpreting numerical data using line plots. The focus is also on describing the shape of the data.

Additional Resource: *Representing Numerical Data,* pages 168–169 (See Curriculum Unit 2)

Understanding the Mathematics

Students make line plots that accurately reflect a given set of data. They use one half as a benchmark (e.g., "less than half of our class has been at this school for three or more years"). Students also use data terms such as *mode, range,* and *outlier* to describe what's typical or atypical about a set of data. They see and describe similarities and differences between two sets of data, and may be comfortable using one line plot to represent both sets.

Option: Assign the **Extension** activity.

Partially Understanding the Mathematics

Students make line plots that accurately represent a given set of data, but may not yet use a consistent scale (e.g., leaving numbers out where there are no data). They are beginning to think about and use one half as a benchmark and to describe important features of the data (e.g., the highest or lowest value, places where there is a lot or a little data, the mode) to describe a set of data. Comparing two sets of data by seeing the big picture of each group may be challenging.

Option: Assign the **Practice** activity.

Not Understanding the Mathematics

Students are just learning to use line plots to represent a set of numerical data. They may represent the data out of order, have trouble setting up a line plot, lose the connection between the Xs and the data they represent, omit pieces of data, or skip values in their line plot. Most students can describe a particular piece of data (e.g., four people have three people living in their home), but they have trouble seeing and describing the shape of the data.

Option: Assign the **Intervention** activity.

Investigation 2 Quiz

In addition to your observations and students' work in Investigation 2, the Quiz (R10) can be used to gather more information.

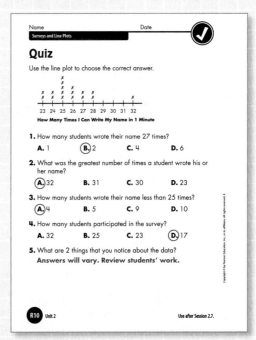

Intervention

20 MIN   INDIVIDUALS

How Many Crayons?

Use anytime after Session 2.2.

Math Focus Points

◆ Using a line plot to represent ordered, numerical data

◆ Reading and interpreting a representation of ordered, numerical data

Vocabulary: data, line plot

Materials: blank paper or M16

Introduce the following problem. Denzel decided to do an experiment in his classroom to find the number of crayons in a box. He took 10 boxes of crayons and counted how many crayons were in each box. Here are the data he collected.

Box	Number of Crayons	Box	Number of Crayons
A	5	F	10
B	5	G	7
C	5	H	5
D	7	I	4
E	5	J	5

Let's think about what a line plot for this data would look like.

What is the fewest number of crayons? What is the greatest number? What does that mean about what numbers should be on our line plot?

Support students in creating a line plot on Half-Inch Grid Paper (M16) or blank paper. Then, students complete their line plots. Be sure students are using Xs that are about the same size.

Finally, discuss the data as a group and/or in pairs. Focus on the following questions:

◆ What do you notice about the data?

◆ How many crayons do most of the boxes have? How do you know?

Students might say:

"Only one box has 10 crayons."

"The number 5 has the most Xs, so I know that most of the boxes have 5 crayons."

ELL **English Language Learners**

Suggest a Sequence Some students may benefit from a suggested sequence, such as the following. *First*, create a line plot with all of the numbers between the smallest and the largest values. *Then*, add an X to show each piece of data. *Last*, count how many Xs each number has.

Additional Resource

Student Math Handbook pages 95–96

Practice

20 MIN   INDIVIDUALS

Representing and Describing Data

Use anytime after Session 2.2.

Math Focus Points

◆ Using a line plot to represent ordered, numerical data

◆ Describing the shape of ordered, numerical data: where data are spread out or concentrated, where there are few data, highest and lowest values, and outliers

Vocabulary: data, line plot, outlier, range, median

Materials: blank paper, R11

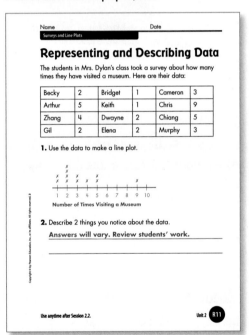

Introduce the data about the number of times a group of students has flown on an airplane.

Jung	0	Pilar	1	Ines	1	Gil	0
Kenji	2	Denzel	0	Keisha	2	Edwin	0
Adam	0	Nancy	1	Gina	0	Nicholas	3
Kelley	0	Oscar	6	Keith	0	Kim	2
Jane	0	Benjamin	0	Becky	0	Elena	1

If you were going to make a line plot of this data, what numbers would you need? Where should the line plot start? Where should it end? What should you do to show how often students have flown on an airplane?

Students construct a line plot to represent the data. Then, discuss what the data show with questions like the following:

◆ Where are the data concentrated?

◆ Where are there few data?

◆ Are there any outliers?

◆ Can you use the word *half* to help you describe the data?

◆ Is there something you notice about most of these students?

Students might say:

"More than half of the students have never flown on an airplane."

"The number 6 is an outlier because there are not a lot of data there."

If students do not mention the range of the data or the median, ask: What is the range of the data? How can you find the median? Then, distribute copies of Representing and Describing Data (R11).

ELL English Language Learners

Provide a Word List Make a permanent chart of important data vocabulary that includes words such as *data, line plot, outlier, range,* and *median.* Review the meaning of each word and help students write or draw examples to serve as a reminder of each word's meaning.

Additional Resource

Student Math Handbook pages 97–98

Extension

30 MIN   GROUPS

Comparing Two Sets of Data
Use anytime after Session 2.4.

Math Focus Points

◆ Using a line plot, bar graph, or other representation to represent ordered, numerical data

◆ Using data to compare groups

Materials: blank paper, R12

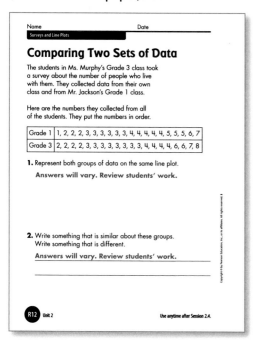

Introduce the data about the number of vowels in the first and last names in one class. Here are the data for the girls' names and the data for the boys' names. I put the numbers in order.

Girls	2, 2, 2, 3, 3, 5, 5, 5, 5, 6
Boys	2, 4, 4, 4, 4, 5, 5, 5, 5, 5

Nancy's name has 2 vowels. Her number 2 is in the list here with all of the other girls who have 2 vowels in their first and last names. How many other girls have 2 vowels in their name?

How would you show both sets of data on a double-bar graph? What would the key show?

Students might say:

 "I would use red bars to show the boys' data and orange for the girls'. The key would show what each color represents."

You can show both sets of data on a line plot too. What could you use on a line plot instead of Xs?

Students might say:

 "I would use B for boys and G for girls."

Once some ideas have been discussed, students use either bar graphs or line plots to show both sets of data on one representation. Assist as needed.

Discuss what students notice about the data, encouraging them to compare the groups. If there is time, compare a double-bar graph to a line plot showing both sets of data. Do they highlight different aspects of the data?

Distribute copies of Comparing Two Sets of Data (R12).

Provide Sentence Stems Some students may have difficulty verbalizing how they graphed the data. Help students by providing sentence stems. For example: First, I _____. Then, I _____. To compare the data, I _____.

Additional Resource

Student Math Handbook pages 99–103

Differentiation in Investigation 3

Mathematics in This Investigation

The mathematics focuses on measuring length and distance with standard units. This includes understanding where to start and stop measuring, how to align and iterate the measuring tool, and how to report measurements in feet and inches.

Understanding the Mathematics

Students have a solid sense of the size of an inch and a foot. They have accurate strategies for measuring distances, including those longer than the measuring tool. Students see why different strategies would result in different measurements. They understand the relationship between feet and inches, and they can think about their results in inches; feet and inches; and yards, feet and inches.

Option: Assign the Extension activity.

Partially Understanding the Mathematics

Students have a fairly accurate sense of the size of an inch and a foot. They have strategies for accurately measuring a distance, but may struggle when that distance is longer than the tool they are using to measure it. They may at first be puzzled that people using the same tool to measure the same distance get different results. They are developing an understanding of the relationship between feet and inches (e.g., 18 inches = 1 foot 6 inches = $1\frac{1}{2}$ feet).

Option: Assign the Practice activity.

Not Understanding the Mathematics

Students are developing a sense of the size of standard units. They understand what it means to measure length or distance, but are still developing strategies for measuring accurately. They may measure from the wrong end of the ruler, not align the ruler properly in relation to the object or distance to be measured, or have difficulty with lengths longer than their measurement tool. They may have a hard time remembering and using information about the relationship between feet and inches in their work.

Option: Assign the Intervention activity.

Investigation 3 Quiz

In addition to your observations and students' work in Investigation 3, the Quiz (R13) can be used to gather more information.

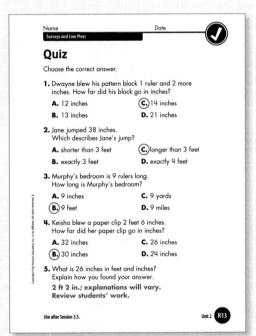

Intervention

20 MIN   INDIVIDUALS

Measuring with a Ruler
Use anytime after Session 3.1.

Math Focus Points
◆ Measuring in inches

Vocabulary: length, inch, feet

Materials: 12-inch rulers, unsharpened pencil

Work with individual students who need additional support when measuring.

Some students may need assistance aligning a ruler with an object when measuring. Model an incorrect method for measuring an unsharpened pencil using a mistake you've seen the student make.

I am going to find the length of this new pencil. What do you think of the way I am measuring?

Discuss why your method is problematic and ask the student to align the pencil correctly.

So it's important to align the end of the pencil with the end of the ruler. Now, about how long is the pencil? What number is the other end of the pencil closest to?

Some students may have trouble measuring a distance longer than a ruler. Help them use multiple rulers to measure your desk.

I'm going to use these rulers to measure the length of my desk.

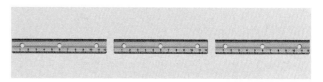

What do you think about the way I am measuring?

Discuss the importance of placing the rulers in a straight line with no gaps or overlaps. Then, work together to calculate the length of the desk. How many whole rulers did you use? What part of the last ruler did you use? How can we figure out the length in feet and inches?

ELL   English Language Learners

Model Thinking Aloud Some students may have difficulty verbalizing how they measured. As you demonstrate how to measure an object, model your thinking aloud. For example: Hold up a book. I want to measure this book. First, I line up the edge of the book with the end of the ruler. Then I look to see what number the other end of the book is closest to. The book is [10] inches long. Repeat for an object longer than a ruler. Be sure to emphasize the importance of placing the rulers in a straight line with no gaps or overlaps.

Additional Resource

Student Math Handbook page 108

Practice

20 MIN | **INDIVIDUALS**

More Feet and Inches
Use anytime after Session 3.3.

Math Focus Points

◆ Understanding the relationship between feet and inches

◆ Using the correct notation to write a measurement in feet and inches

Materials: 12-inch rulers, R14

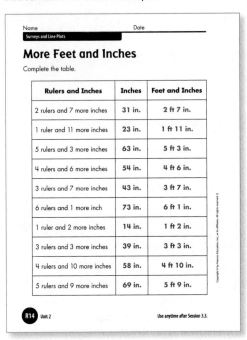

Name _____ Date _____

Surveys and Line Plots

More Feet and Inches

Complete the table.

Rulers and Inches	Inches	Feet and Inches
2 rulers and 7 more inches	31 in.	2 ft 7 in.
1 ruler and 11 more inches	23 in.	1 ft 11 in.
5 rulers and 3 more inches	63 in.	5 ft 3 in.
4 rulers and 6 more inches	54 in.	4 ft 6 in.
3 rulers and 7 more inches	43 in.	3 ft 7 in.
6 rulers and 1 more inch	73 in.	6 ft 1 in.
1 ruler and 2 more inches	14 in.	1 ft 2 in.
3 rulers and 3 more inches	39 in.	3 ft 3 in.
4 rulers and 10 more inches	58 in.	4 ft 10 in.
5 rulers and 9 more inches	69 in.	5 ft 9 in.

R14 Unit 2   Use anytime after Session 3.3.

Distribute a ruler to each student or pair. Read the following problem aloud. A Grade 3 class was playing Blowing a Paper Clip. It is played just like Blowing a Pattern Block. They measured how far each student blew the paper clip. Here are some of their data.

Oscar: 1 ruler and 5 more inches

Kim: 1 ruler

Adam: 2 rulers and half a ruler

Gina: 1 ruler and 10 more inches

How far did Oscar blow the paper clip? Talk with someone next to you for a minute. Then, discuss students' responses to your question.

Students might say:

"17 inches because one ruler is 12 inches and 12 plus 5 is 17."

"1 foot and 5 inches because a ruler is 1 foot."

Be sure to discuss the equivalence of 1 foot and 12 inches. Then students find how far the rest of the students blew the paper clip. Collect and discuss students' answers, recording them on the board in both inches and feet and inches.

Oscar: 17 inches or 1 foot 5 inches

Kim: 12 in. or 1 ft

Adam: 30 inches or 2 feet 6 inches or $2\frac{1}{2}$ feet

Gina: 22" or 1' 10"

Distribute copies of More Feet and Inches (R14).

ELL English Language Learners

Provide a Word List Review which words and symbols go with which measurements. Help students connect words, abbreviations, and symbols to the measurements they represent. For example: This eraser is about 2 inches long. Show me with your fingers about how long an inch is. Can you show me 1 inch on a ruler? 2 inches? To record the length of this eraser, we would write 2 inches or 2 in. or 2".

Additional Resource

Student Math Handbook page 109

20 MIN | **PAIRS**

Extension

Yards, Feet, and Inches

Use anytime after Session 3.2.

Math Focus Points

◆ Measuring lengths longer than the measuring tool

◆ Understanding the relationship between feet and inches

◆ Combining feet and inches to get a total measurement

Vocabulary: yard

Materials: yardsticks (1 per pair), 12-inch rulers (1 per pair), blank paper, R15

Name _____ Date _____
Surveys and Line Plots

Yards, Feet, and Inches

Solve the problems, and show your work.

1. The desk is 3 feet 11 inches wide. How wide is it in yards, feet, and inches?

   1 yard, 11 inches; review students' work.

2. Justin is 5 feet 1 inch tall. How tall is he in yards, feet, and inches?

   1 yard, 2 feet, 1 inch; review students' work.

3. The path from the window to the door measures 12 feet 8 inches. How long is the path in yards, feet, and inches?

   4 yards, 8 inches; review students' work.

4. The sidewalk from the bus stop to the door measures 22 feet 3 inches. How long is the sidewalk in yards, feet, and inches?

   7 yards, 1 foot, 3 inches; review students' work.

Use anytime after Session 3.2. | Unit 2 **R15**

Students measure the length of the board in feet and inches, in all inches, and in yards, feet, and inches. Briefly review methods for measuring distances longer than a ruler or yardstick, and the relationship between feet, yards, and inches. Write the following on the board for students to copy.

_____ feet and _____ inches

_____ inches

_____ yards, _____ feet, and _____ inches

Pairs should decide what measurement tool to use.

End by discussing students' solutions and strategies. How many feet and inches long is the whiteboard? Come to an agreement about the length of the board, encouraging a pair or two to model their method(s). If the board is 8 feet 2 inches, how many inches would it be?

Students might say:

"Every foot is 12 inches. So I added 8 12's and then the extra 2 inches."

What is the length in yards, feet, and inches? How did you figure that out?

Students might say:

"I know there are 3 feet in a yard. So, there are 2 yards in 8 feet with 2 feet leftover. And then there's still the 2 inches."

Distribute copies of Yards, Feet, and Inches (R15).

ELL English Language Learners

Provide Sentence Stems Some students may confuse the equivalencies for yards, feet, and inches. Write the following on the board:

◆ _____ inches = _____ feet

◆ _____ feet = _____ yards

Ask students to help you fill in the correct numbers. Then, post it for students to use as a reference.

Additional Resource

Student Math Handbook page 105

Differentiation in Investigation 1

Mathematics in This Investigation

The mathematics focuses on extending place-value ideas to 1,000 and using the ideas about 1s, 10s, and 100s to estimate and solve addition and subtraction problems.

Understanding the Mathematics

Students accurately locate numbers on a 1,000 chart. They know what page a number will be on and use multiples of 10 as landmarks for navigation. They put 2- and 3-digit numbers in order easily. They use knowledge about place value and the way numbers are written to solve problems about the number of 10s in larger 3-digit numbers. To figure out the number of 100s in an addition problem, they combine the 100s and then consider whether the 10s and 1s make another hundred, using knowledge of combinations that make 10 and 100. They use similar knowledge to add 2-digit numbers, to make two 2-digit numbers with a total as close as possible to 100, and to find the difference between 2- and 3-digit numbers.

Option: Assign the Extension activity.

Partially Understanding the Mathematics

Students use multiples of 10 and 100 to locate numbers on a 1,000 chart, but they do not consistently see the relationship between the numbers on it (e.g., 49, 149, 249). They are beginning to use knowledge about the number of 10s in 100 to solve problems about the number of 10s in larger 3-digit numbers. To figure out the number of 100s in an addition problem, they combine the 100s, but they may be just starting to realize that the number of 10s and 1s can result in another hundred. They more consistently make two 2-digit numbers whose total is as close as possible to 100, but occasionally they do not realize that there are combinations that land exactly on, or get closer to, 100.

Option: Assign the Practice activity.

Not Understanding the Mathematics

Students locate numbers on a 1,000 chart with effort. They may not know what page a given number will be on, treat each number as a new and individual case, and do a lot of counting by 1s. They count by 10s to find the number of 10s in larger 3-digit numbers. They look only at the 100s place to estimate the number of 100s. They may make two 2-digit numbers whose sum is close to 100, but they don't consider more than one option or realize that there are combinations that land exactly on, or get closer to, 100. They may need to model addition and subtraction problems with stickers or their 1,000 chart.

Option: Assign the Intervention activity.

Investigation 1 Quiz

In addition to your observations and students' work in Investigation 1, the Quiz (R16) can be used to gather more information.

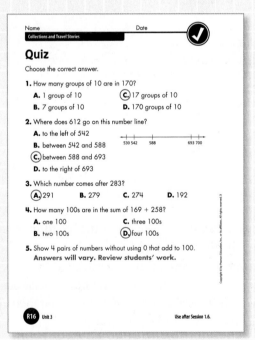

Intervention

20 MIN **INDIVIDUALS**

Finding Groups of 10

Use anytime after Session 1.4.

Math Focus Points

◆ Recognizing and representing the groups of 10s in 3-digit numbers

Materials: completed 1,000 charts (from Session 1.1)

Remind students of the problems on *Student Activity Book* pages 10–11, in which they determined how many groups of 10 are in 3-digit numbers.

Each problem asked you to find how many groups of 10 are in a 3-digit number. I noticed that you counted by 10s. That is one way to do it, but it can take a long time to count that high.

Pose a new problem to think about.

> I have 482 pennies. How many stacks of 10 can I make? How many single pennies will I have left?

Let's think first about what we know. How many 10s are in 100? If there are 10 tens in 100, can that help us to figure out how many 10s are in 200?

Students might say:

"There are ten 10s in 100. Another 100 would be ten more 10s. So there are twenty 10s in 200."

Ask students to use the same reasoning to figure out how many 10s are in 300 and in 400.

You figured out that there are forty 10s in 400. How many more 10s are in the number 482? How do you know?

Students might say:

"There are 8 tens in 82: 10, 20, 30, 40, 50, 60, 70, 80."

How many stacks of 10 can I make? How many pennies will I have left?

Elicit that there are 48 stacks of 10 pennies and 2 single pennies. Then help students check their answers using their completed 1,000 chart. Ask questions such as the following:

◆ How many 10s are in the 100 chart?

◆ How many 10s are in the 200 chart? How many 10s is that so far?

◆ How many 10s are in the 300 chart? How many 10s is that now?

◆ How many 10s are in the 400 chart? How many 10s is that now?

◆ Find 482 on the 500 chart. How many more 10s are there?

◆ How many 10s in all? How many 1s?

Model Thinking Aloud If students are having difficulty, relate the problem to a situation with which they are more familiar. Model the actions described. To find the number of 10s in 327, I thought about stickers. I need three sheets to show 300. There are 1, 2, 3, 4, 5, 6, 7, 8, 9, 10 strips of 10 in a sheet of 100. So three sheets would have 10, 20, 30 strips of 10. Then 27 is two strips of 10 and 7 singles. So, there are thirty-two 10s and seven 1s in 327.

Additional Resource

Student Math Handbook pages 7–8

Practice

Addition and the 900 Chart
Use anytime after Session 1.1.

Math Focus Points

◆ Reading, writing, and sequencing numbers to 1,000

Materials: M6 (1 per group), R17

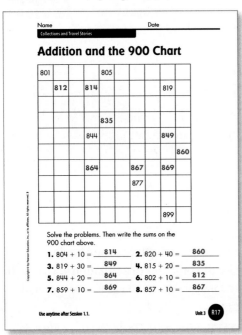

Name _____ Date _____
Collections and Travel Stories

Addition and the 900 Chart

801			805						
	812	814					819		
			835						
		844					849		
									860
		864		867	869				
				877					
					899				

Solve the problems. Then write the sums on the 900 chart above.

1. 804 + 10 = __814__   2. 820 + 40 = __860__
3. 819 + 30 = __849__   4. 815 + 20 = __835__
5. 844 + 20 = __864__   6. 802 + 10 = __812__
7. 859 + 10 = __869__   8. 857 + 10 = __867__

Use anytime after Session 1.1.   Unit 3 R17

Materials to Prepare: Prepare a 900 chart from page 5 of the 1,000 Chart (M6). Fill in the numbers 806, 834, 848, and 882. Cross out the 1,000 section. Make a copy for each group.

801					806				810
		834							
						848			
882									
									900

900

Remind students of the work they did on the 1,000 chart. You constructed your 1,000 chart from 100 charts and have been working on locating different numbers on it.

Distribute copies of the 900 chart to students. Explain that the 1,000 section is crossed out because they will only be using the 900 chart today.

Write 848 + 10 = _____ on the board. Students find the sum and write it on their 900 charts. How did you find the sum? How did you find that number on the chart?

Students might say:

"The sum is 858. I found 848 on the chart. Each row is 10, so I just moved down 1 row to 858."

Repeat for 834 + 20 = _____,
806 + 50 = _____, and 882 + 10 = _____.

Distribute copies of Addition and the 900 Chart (R17).

ELL English Language Learners

Partner Talk Have pairs work together to explain how they located a sum on the 900 chart. Encourage more proficient speakers to use words such as *column*, *row*, *tens*, *more*, and *sum*. Less proficient speakers will likely use short phrases and can point to the chart to explain.

Additional Resource
Student Math Handbook page 14

Extension

20 MIN   PAIRS

Sequencing Numbers in Four Categories

Use anytime after Session 1.3.

Math Focus Points

◆ Reading, writing, and sequencing numbers to 1,000

Materials: Collection Cards (1 deck per pair), blank paper (1 sheet per pair), 1,000 charts, R18

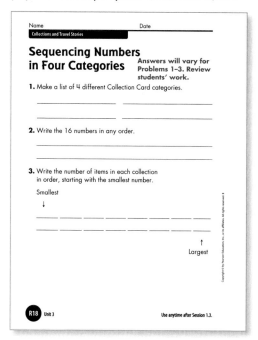

Remind students of the problems they solved involving the Collection Cards in Session 1.2. You chose two categories, which gave you 8 cards. You used the number of items on each card and put them in order from smallest to largest.

Write 8 numbers on the board.

125	257	36	304
82	310	140	207

Imagine that these are the number of items on your 8 cards. How can you start to sequence the numbers?

Students might say:

"I would start with the smallest numbers. 36 and 82 don't have any hundreds, so they are the smallest, and 36 is less than 82."

"Put the smallest number and the largest number on a number line. So put 36 at the left end, and 310 at the right end."

Today's activity is similar, but you will be sequencing numbers in four of the categories.

Distribute Collection Cards and blank paper to each pair. Students choose four categories, pull out all of the cards in those categories, and put the numbers in order from least to greatest. They record the sequence of numbers and then find those numbers on their 1,000 charts.

Distribute copies of Sequencing Numbers in Four Categories (R18).

ELL English Language Learners

Rephrase Remind students that when they are sequencing the cards, they are placing the numbers in order from smallest to largest. 36 is the smallest number because it has the least number of tens. The largest number will have the most hundreds, tens, and ones.

Additional Resource

Student Math Handbook pages 10–11

Differentiation in Investigation 2

Mathematics in This Investigation

The mathematics focuses on accurately adding 2- and 3-digit numbers by developing strategies that rely on knowledge of place value and on breaking numbers apart.

Understanding the Mathematics

Students are comfortable adding multiples of 10 and 100 to 3-digit numbers through 300. They understand and can use more than one strategy (e.g., adding by place, adding one number on in parts, or making an equivalent problem) to efficiently add 2- and 3-digit numbers accurately. Given the first step of an addition problem, students figure out what part of the problem remains to be solved, and they get the correct solution.

Option: Assign the **Extension** activity.

Partially Understanding the Mathematics

Students are becoming comfortable adding multiples of 10 and 100 to 3-digit numbers through 300. They break numbers apart to add them, but they are still developing their ability to do so efficiently. For example, they may break numbers into 10s rather than use multiples of 10. They are able to keep track of the parts of the problem. It is challenging for students to try to use a different strategy than the one they typically use.

Option: Assign the **Practice** activity.

Not Understanding the Mathematics

Students have difficulty adding multiples of 10 and 100. They may be more comfortable with numbers to 100, and have trouble with larger numbers. They may not see ways to break numbers apart to add them, or they do so in inefficient ways and then have trouble keeping track of the parts. They may need to use stickers or 1,000 books to directly model addition problems.

Option: Assign the **Intervention** activity.

Investigation 2 Quiz

In addition to your observations and students' work in Investigation 2, the Quiz (R19) can be used to gather more information.

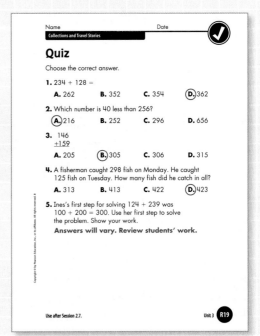

Intervention

20 MIN   INDIVIDUALS

Modeling Solutions to Addition Problems

Use anytime after Session 2.4.

Math Focus Points

◆ Solving addition problems with 2- and 3-digit numbers (up to 400) by breaking numbers apart and recombining them

◆ Developing strategies for solving addition problems by focusing on how each strategy starts

If students are having difficulty solving addition problems involving 3-digit numbers, work with them on an easier problem to determine whether the issue is the size of the numbers or the lack of an effective addition strategy.

Let's find the sum of 36 + 59. Take a minute to look at this problem. How many 10s do you think there will be in the answer?

Students might say:

"8 tens because 30 + 50 = 80."

Work together to model 36 + 59 with cubes or stickers. You said that there would be 8 tens because 30 + 50 = 80. Can you show me that first step with [cubes, stickers]? Then focus students' attention on the ones. What do we have left to take care of now? How many 1s are there?

Students might say:

"I still have to add 6 ones and 9 ones. So I have to add 15 more."

Once you have agreed on a solution, help students record the work they've done, first with sticker notation and then with equations.

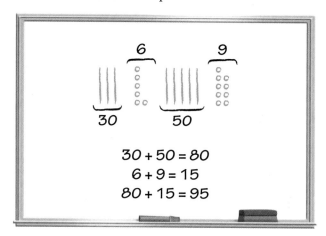

ELL **English Language Learners**

Rephrase Ask the questions in the activity again, but in a shorter, simpler form. For example:

◆ How can you start?

◆ What would you do next?

◆ What do you have left to do?

Additional Resource

Student Math Handbook pages 20–24

Practice

20 MIN   PAIRS

Using Addition Strategies
Use anytime after Session 2.2.

Math Focus Points

◆ Solving addition problems with 2- and 3-digit numbers (up to 400) by breaking numbers apart and recombining them

◆ Representing addition strategies

Materials: completed 1,000 charts (from Session 1.1; optional), R20

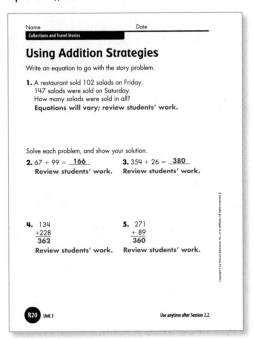

Here's a problem. Work with a partner to solve it.

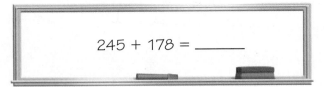

$$245 + 178 = \underline{\qquad}$$

Give pairs a few minutes to work, and then ask volunteers to share. As students describe their strategies, restate what they did to begin, and encourage others to think about what they might have done next. [Edwin] and [Bridget] started with $200 + 100$. They added the 100s in the problem first. What do you think they did next?

As each strategy is shared, ask students how they used or could use a number line, sticker sketches, or a 1,000 chart to represent a particular solution.

Students might say:

"We used stickers to show each number, then we counted the 100s, then the 10s, and then the 1s."

Record this (or any other) strategy on the board.

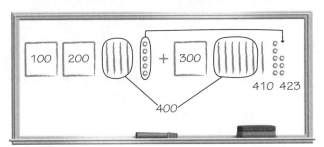

[Ines] and [Philip] started with $245 + 55$. They kept one number whole and broke the other number apart to get to a multiple of 10. What do you think they did next?

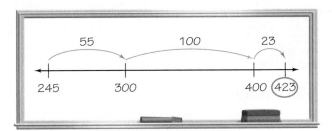

Distribute copies of Using Addition Strategies (R20).

ELL   English Language Learners

Partner Talk Have pairs explain their strategies to each other. Encourage more proficient speakers to use complete sentences and to use words such as *add*, *sum*, and *multiple of 10*. Less proficient speakers can use short phrases or their native language to express their ideas, and can point to the steps on their papers.

Additional Resource

Student Math Handbook pages 20–24

Extension

20 MIN PAIRS

Creating Starter Problems

Use anytime after Session 2.5.

Math Focus Points

◆ Developing strategies for solving addition problems by focusing on how each strategy starts

◆ Solving addition problems with 2- and 3-digit numbers (up to 400) by breaking numbers apart and recombining them

Materials: R21

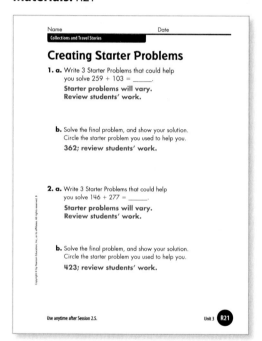

Remind students of their work with Starter Problems in Session 2.5. You solved three starter problems and then determined how you could use one of them to solve the final problem in the set.

Today you will be given only the final problem. Your job is to write three starter problems that could be used to find the solution. What makes a good starter problem?

Students might say:

"A problem that you can solve quickly and easily in your head."

What strategies could you use to create the starter problems?

Students might say:

"Think about how you'd solve the problem. Then write down your first step."

Write the following on the board.

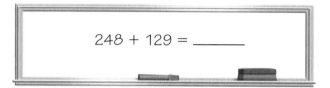

$$248 + 129 = \rule{2cm}{0.4pt}$$

This is your final problem. Write three different starter problems for it. Then swap papers with your partner and use one of his or her starter problems to solve the final problem. Circle the starter problem you used.

Give pairs time to work. Share a few starter problems and solution strategies on the board.

Distribute copies of Creating Starter Problems (R21).

ELL English Language Learners

Use Repetition Make a list of possible strategies to use for creating starter problems and give an example of each. Strategies that can be on the list include adding by place, keeping one number whole, and changing the numbers. Read through the list with students, pointing to the numbers in the examples to emphasize the meanings of the terms. Repeat with other examples of each strategy, as needed.

Additional Resource

Student Math Handbook pages 20–24

Differentiation in Investigation 3

Mathematics in This Investigation

The mathematics focuses on adding or subtracting to find the difference between 2 and 3-digit numbers, and on using 100 as an important landmark in solving such problems.

Understanding the Mathematics

Students represent subtraction on a number line and use addition or subtraction to represent and solve problems about difference. They can make a 2-digit and a 3-digit number as close as possible to 100, and find the difference between those numbers, using 100 as a landmark. They are fluent adding and subtracting multiples of 10.

Option: Assign the Extension activity.

Partially Understanding the Mathematics

Students represent subtraction on a number line, but may be more comfortable conceptualizing problems about difference as addition (e.g., 56 + 88 = 144) rather than subtraction (e.g., 144 − 88 =56). They can make 2-digit and 3-digit numbers that are close to 100, though occasionally not as close as possible. They find the difference between those numbers, often using 100 as a landmark. They can add and subtract 10, but are still developing fluency with adding and subtracting multiples of 10.

Option: Assign the Practice activity.

Not Understanding the Mathematics

Students may find it difficult to make sense of problems about subtraction, particularly when presented on a number line that does not show each individual number in the problem (as compared to a 200 chart). They may directly model the situation each time, and may see it as addition only (e.g., how many more do I need to get to X?). They can make 2-digit and 3-digit numbers that are close to 100 (though often not as close as possible), and may count by 1s to find the difference between those numbers and 100. They are still developing fluency with adding and subtracting 10.

Option: Assign the Intervention activity.

Investigation 3 Quiz

In addition to your observations and students' work in Investigation 3, the Quiz (R22) can be used to gather more information.

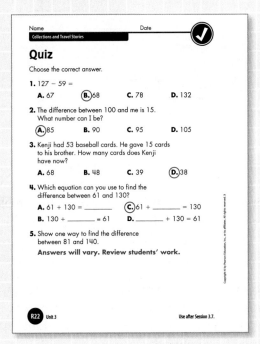

Intervention

20 MIN   **INDIVIDUALS**

Number Lines and the 200 Chart

Use anytime after Session 3.2.

Math Focus Points

- Finding the difference between 2- and 3-digit numbers and 100
- Using multiples of 100 as a landmark to solve subtraction problems

Materials: M53

Write the following problem on the board and read it aloud.

> The difference between 100 and me is 17. What numbers can I be?

Distribute a 200 Chart (M53) to each student to use as needed to find the answers to this riddle.

What's one number that fits this riddle? How did you figure that out?

Students might say:

"I used the 200 chart. I started at 100 and jumped back 10 to 90. Then I jumped back 7 more and that got me to 83."

Let's look at your strategy on a number line. Where did you start on the 200 Chart? Where would you start on a number line? Work together to show the jumps the student took.

Ask questions that help students understand the relationship between the 200 chart and a number line.

- How big was your first jump on the 200 chart? How big should the first jump be on the number line?
- Where did the first jump end on the 200 chart? Where will the first jump land on the number line?
- Where did your second jump end on the 200 chart? Where will the second jump land on the number line?

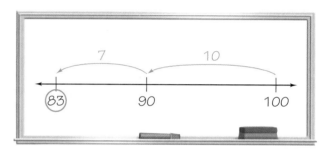

Repeat the process to show the other answer, $100 + 17 = 117$, on another number line.

If time remains, work together to find the difference between 83 and 117, modeling the use of 100 as a helpful landmark on the number line.

ELL) **English Language Learners**

Partner Talk Pairs discuss how the 200 chart and/or the number line helped them. Beginning ELLs may only be able to complete the activity with a partner from their language group in their native language. Listen for and help students use correct vocabulary.

Additional Resource

Student Math Handbook pages 29–30

Practice

20 MIN **PAIRS**

"Less Than" Questions
Use anytime after Session 3.4.

Math Focus Points
◆ Finding the difference between two numbers by either adding or subtracting

Materials: R23

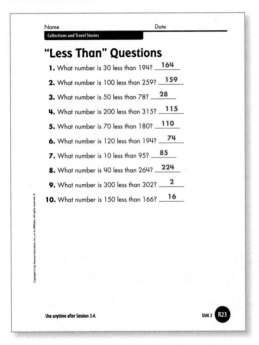

Write the following problem on the board.

What number is 40 less than 136?

Give pairs a few minutes to find the answer. How did you find the answer? Did you use addition or subtraction?

Students might say:

"I used subtraction. I know that 136 − 10 = 126. 126 − 10 = 116 and 116 − 10 = 106. And I still have one more 10 to subtract. 106 − 10 = 96."

"I used addition. 40 plus 60 gets me to 100 and then I needed to add 36 more to get to 136. 60 and 36 is 96."

Write the following questions on the board.

What number is 20 less than 157?

What number is 60 less than 281?

What number is 100 less than 216?

What number is 300 less than 524?

What number is 120 less than 235?

Work with your partner to find the answers to these questions. After students have finished, have volunteers share their solution strategies for each.

Distribute copies of "Less Than" Questions (R23).

ELL **English Language Learners**

Model Thinking Aloud Students may benefit from working through a problem one-on-one. As you work with the student, model your thinking aloud.

To find what number is 20 less than 157, I can use subtraction. I know 157 − 10 = 147. Then, I need to subtract one more 10. 147 − 10 = 137. So, 20 less than 157 is 137. Or, 157 minus 20 is 137.

Have the student solve the problem and then support him or her in describing his or her steps.

Additional Resource

Student Math Handbook
Game: *How Far From 100?* SMH G15
Materials: Digit Cards, M55

Extension

20 MIN   PAIRS

How Far from 100?

Use anytime after Session 3.5.

Math Focus Points

◆ Using multiples of 100 as a landmark to solve subtraction problems

Materials: Digit Cards (1 deck per pair), M55, R24

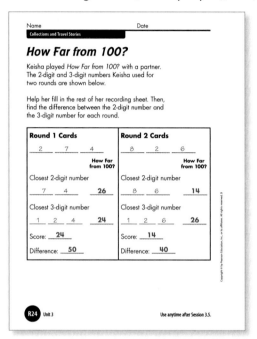

Tell students that there is a new rule for playing *How Far from 100?* After you find your score, you are to find the difference between your 2-digit number and your 3-digit number.

Suppose your numbers are 94 and 124. What is the difference between these numbers? In other words, how far is it from 94 to 124?

Give students a few minutes to find the answer before discussing solution strategies.

Students might say:

"I know that from 94 to 100 is 6 and from 100 to 124 is 24, so the difference is 6 + 24 and that's 30."

"124 − 24 = 100. Then I had to subtract 6 more to get to 94, so I subtracted 30 in all."

Students now play a few rounds of the game, implementing the new rule as described. They will need a copy of the *How Far from 100?* Recording Sheet (M55). Explain that they can record the difference in the space below their score.

Distribute copies of *How Far from 100?* (R24).

ELL ⟩ English Language Learners

Suggest a Sequence To help students understand the new rules, suggest the following sequence of steps. For Beginner ELLs who need more support, play a round with them to model each of the steps.

1. Play a round of *How Far from 100?*

2. Find your score.

3. Find the difference between your 2-digit number and your 3-digit number.

4. Record the difference on the back of your recording sheet.

Additional Resource

Student Math Handbook pages 31–35

Differentiation in Investigation 4

Mathematics in This Investigation

The mathematics focuses on developing a variety of strategies for solving different types of subtraction problems.

Additional Resource: *Types of Subtraction Situations,* pages 203–204 (See Curriculum Unit 3)

Understanding the Mathematics

Students reason numerically to solve comparison problems and write addition or subtraction equations to represent the situation. They have several strategies (e.g., subtracting one number in parts, adding up, subtracting back) for solving subtraction problems, whether presented in the context of comparison, finding the difference or distance, or removal. They use knowledge about the distance from 100 to reason about the distance from multiples of 100, they use multiples of 100 as landmarks, and they understand and use relationships between problems to reason about the operation of subtraction (e.g., if you subtract 5 more from the same initial amount, 5 fewer will be left).

Option: Assign the **Extension** activity.

Partially Understanding the Mathematics

Students use tools to model comparison problems. They have at least one strategy for solving subtraction problems, though the strategy they choose often depends on the context. They are beginning to use knowledge about the distance from 100 to reason about the distance from multiples of 100 and to use multiples of 100 as landmarks. Reasoning about relationships between subtraction problems (e.g., $85 - 25$ and $85 - 35$), is challenging.

Option: Assign the **Practice** activity.

Not Understanding the Mathematics

Students find it challenging to conceptualize comparison or "how many more?" problems and to figure out what the problems are asking. Students are still working to develop a dependable strategy for subtraction problems. Students may get answers that do not seem unreasonable to them even though the answers are actually far from correct. Some students may be using laborious strategies such as counting mostly by 1s. They are beginning to use knowledge about the distance from 100 and to use 100 as a landmark. They are not yet reasoning about relationships between subtraction problems (e.g. $85 - 25$ and $85 - 35$).

Option: Assign the **Intervention** activity.

Investigation 4 Quiz

In addition to your observations and students' work in Investigation 4, the Quiz (R25) can be used to gather more information.

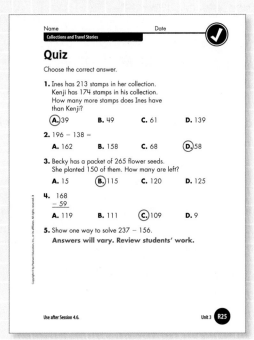

Intervention

20 MIN **INDIVIDUALS**

Using the Number Line

Use anytime after Session 4.2.

Math Focus Points

◆ Using number lines to represent solutions to comparison problems

◆ Finding the difference between two numbers by either adding or subtracting

◆ Solving subtraction story problems that involve comparisons

Vocabulary: add up, subtract back

Materials: cubes in towers of 10 (4 per student)

Present students who are having difficulty comparing two quantities a situation with smaller numbers.

Keisha has 32 stickers.

Pilar has 19 stickers.

How many more stickers does Keisha have than Pilar?

Encourage students to use cubes to model the problem. Can you show me Keisha's stickers? Pilar's stickers? Who has more? Now, what are we trying to figure out? How can we find out how many more stickers Keisha has?

Discuss students' ideas, then ask them to solve the problem. After students have had time to work, ask them to explain their solution strategies, including whether they added up or subtracted back.

Students might say:

"I put the two towers next to each other and counted the extras."

"If you add 1 more to 19, that's 20. Add 10 more and that's 30. And 2 more gets you to 32. I added 1, 10, and 2 so I got 13 altogether."

How could we use a number line to show how you solved the problem? It sounds like you thought of the problem as 19 + _____ = 32. What was your first step?

Ask students to help you draw a number line that shows how the student solved the problem.

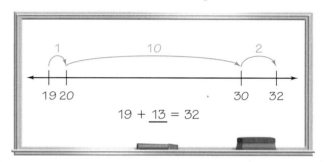

$$19 + \underline{13} = 32$$

Provide similar problems with numbers under 40 for students to solve.

⬤ ELL ⬤ **English Language Learners**

Suggest a Sequence Ask guiding questions to help students verbalize the steps they used to solve the problem. Summarize students' reasoning after each step. For example: What did you do *first*? Oh. You added 1 to 19. Why did you do that? I see. You wanted to get to a multiple of 10. What did you do *next*? Oh, you added 10. What did you do *after that*?

Additional Resource

Student Math Handbook pages 26–28

Practice

20 MIN   PAIRS

More Subtraction Problems

Use anytime after Session 4.5.

Math Focus Points

◆ Solving subtraction problems with 2- and 3-digit numbers (up to 300) using strategies that involve either subtracting one number in parts, adding up, or subtracting back

Materials: completed 1,000 Charts (from Session 1.1, as needed), R26

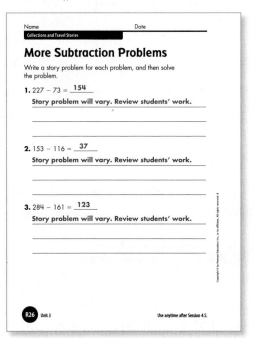

Write the following problem on the board.

$$178 - 109 = \underline{\qquad}$$

Talk with your partner to make up a story for this problem. You can write a story about removing or taking away one part from a total, comparing two amounts, or finding how many more are needed to make the missing part. Ask a few volunteers to share their stories, highlighting the different types.

Ask students to solve the problem. Then, discuss and compare the strategies and tools students used.

Students might say:

"I took 109 away from 178 in chunks. First I did 178 − 100. Then I subtracted 9."

"I used a number line to add up from 109 to 178. I did 109 + 1 = 110, 110 + 60 got me to 170, and I still needed 8 more. I added on 1 and 60 and 8, and that's 69 altogether."

Let's think about what [Kim's] number line would look like.

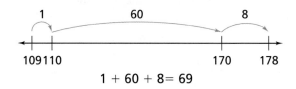

$$1 + 60 + 8 = 69$$

Write the following equations on the board and repeat the process: $220 - 57 = \underline{\qquad}$, $149 - 126 = \underline{\qquad}$, and $191 - 94 = \underline{\qquad}$.

Distribute copies of More Subtraction Problems (R26).

ELL English Language Learners

Use Repetition Make a list of the three categories of subtraction situations:

◆ removal or take away

◆ comparing or comparison

◆ missing part

Make up and record a simple story problem to illustrate each. Act out the story problems with students, as needed.

Additional Resource

Student Math Handbook pages 26–28

Extension

20 MIN   PAIRS

Comparing Heights of Trees

Use anytime after Session 4.1.

Math Focus Points

◆ Solving subtraction story problems that involve comparison

◆ Understanding comparison as the difference between two numbers

Materials: R27

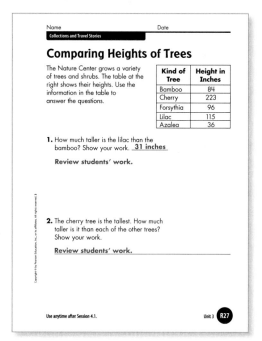

Draw the following table on the board.

Kind of Tree	Height in Inches
Granny Smith	144
Golden delicious	180
Red delicious	from 180 to 240

Ms. Jones has three different apple trees in her yard. This table shows their heights. How much taller is the golden delicious tree than the Granny Smith tree? Give pairs time to solve the problem. Then ask for solutions, strategies, and equations.

Students might say:

 "The golden delicious tree is 36 inches taller. I added up from 144 to 180: 144 plus 30 is 174 plus 6 more equals 180."

 "I got 36 inches too, but I subtracted. I knew $180 - 140 = 40$. Then I still had 4 more to subtract."

Ms. Jones has not measured the red delicious tree but she knows it has a height between 180 and 240 inches. Choose a height for this tree and then figure out how much taller the red delicious tree is than the Granny Smith tree. How does it compare to the golden delicious tree?

Distribute copies of Comparing Heights of Trees (R27).

ELL English Language Learners

Partner Talk Pair ELLs to give them practice with English. Beginning English Language Learners may only be able to say phrases like "I added" or "I subtracted." More proficient speakers can add information to give a more detailed answer. Encourage students to use words such as *compare, add up, subtract back, smaller number,* and *larger number.*

Additional Resource

Student Math Handbook page 28

Differentiation in Investigation 1

Mathematics in This Investigation

The mathematics focuses on developing an understanding of perimeter and on using standard units (inches, feet, yards, centimeters, and meters) to measure the distance around various shapes.

Understanding the Mathematics

Students choose appropriate measurement tools and use them accurately. They understand what perimeter is and may need to measure only two sides of a rectangle to determine the perimeter. They include fractional measurements in their work and are comfortable measuring circular and nonrectangular shapes. Students can draw several different shapes that have the same perimeter, and they think about the length of the sides, rather than the overall size of the shape, to predict and order shapes by perimeter.

Option: Assign the **Extension** activity.

Partially Understanding the Mathematics

Students usually choose appropriate measurement tools and use them accurately most of the time. They understand perimeter as the distance around the edge of a 2-D shape or object. They measure all four sides of a rectangle to determine its perimeter. Adding fractional parts, and finding the perimeter of circles and nonrectangular shapes, may be challenging. Students can draw a shape that has a given perimeter, but they are initially unaware that different-looking shapes can have the same perimeter. Their first instinct in predicting the order of a set of shapes based on perimeter is to consider the size of the shapes or the number of sides, rather than the length of the sides.

Option: Assign the **Practice** activity.

Not Understanding the Mathematics

Students don't yet consistently choose appropriate measurement tools given the lengths to be measured, and they are still developing strategies for accurate measurement. For example, they may measure from the wrong end of the tool, not line up the end of the tool with the end of the length to be measured, leave gaps or overlaps when they move the measurement tool, or have difficulty keeping track of what has been measured. Students are just beginning to understand what perimeter is and how to measure it. Keeping track of the various measurements, and adding them accurately, is a challenge. They likely ignore fractional parts of such measurements. Finding the perimeter of circles and nonrectangular shapes, and drawing a shape with a given perimeter, is quite difficult. They may not realize that more than one shape is possible. Their predictions about the order of a set of shapes based on perimeter seem not to depend on mathematical reasoning.

Option: Assign the **Intervention** activity.

Investigation 1 Quiz

In addition to your observations and students' work in Investigation 1, the Quiz (R28) can be used to gather more information.

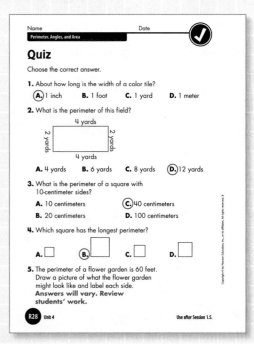

Intervention

20 MIN   PAIRS

Another Ant's Path

Use anytime after Session 1.2.

Math Focus Points

◆ Understanding perimeter as the measure around the outside edges of a 2-dimensional figure

◆ Finding perimeter using standard units

◆ Using U.S. standard and metric units to accurately measure length

Vocabulary: perimeter

Materials: 3″ × 5″ index cards (1 per pair), inch/centimeter rulers (1 per pair)

. . . .

Remind students of their work in determining how far an ant would have to walk to get all the way around the perimeter of a piece of paper.

Hold up an index card. Your job today is to work with your partner to figure out how far the ant would have to walk to get all the way around the perimeter of this index card. Where will the ant start? Where will it end?

Students might say:

"The ant will start at a corner and go all the way around until it gets back to where it started."

Distribute index cards to each pair. Have partners decide which corner their ant will start from and mark that corner with an X. Have each student trace the path of the ant with his or her finger. Start at the corner with an X. Trace around all edges of the card until you get back to where you started.

Discuss ways to ensure accurate measurements. Model students' suggestions and write them on the board. The list should include statements similar to the ones given below.

> Line up the ruler and a corner of the card at zero.
>
> Put the ruler right next to the edge of the card.
>
> Read the measurement carefully.

Now you're going to work with your partner to find the perimeter of the card in inches. Distribute a ruler to each pair and review which is the inch side. You might model the measurement of the first side, showing students how one partner can hold the ruler as the other partner reads the measurement. Partners can then measure the remaining edges on their own.

Discuss students' results and then pose the next problem. Now let's find the perimeter in centimeters.

Support students as they work together to find the perimeter of the card in centimeters. Again, discuss students' results. End by comparing the two measurements and eliciting students' thoughts about the difference.

═══ **ELL** ═══ **English Language Learners**

Provide a Word List Write and illustrate the words *corner, edge, ruler, perimeter, inch,* and *centimeter* on chart paper. Explain the meaning of each using visuals and gestures, then have students explain the meaning in their own words. Encourage them to use these words throughout the activity.

Additional Resource

Student Math Handbook pages 110–111

Practice

20 MIN **GROUPS**

Ordering More Shapes by Perimeter

Use anytime after Session 1.4.

Math Focus Points

◆ Finding perimeter using standard units

◆ Understanding perimeter as the measure around the outside edges of a 2-dimensional figure

Materials: inch/centimeter rulers, string or adding machine tape (as needed), R29

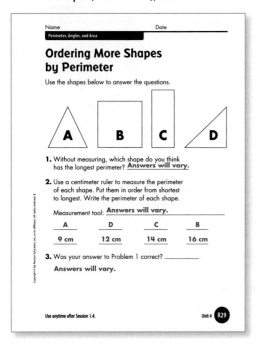

· ·

Draw figures similar to the following shapes on the board. Each shape should have a different perimeter.

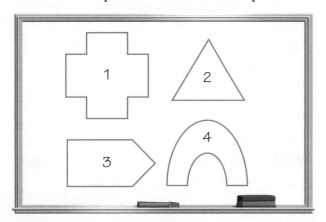

Look at these shapes. Which shape do you think has the shortest perimeter? The longest? Why do you think so?

Students might say:

"I think shape 2 has the shortest perimeter because it only has 3 short sides and Shape 1 has so many sides I think it will be the longest."

Discuss students' predictions, then pose the task. Let's measure to find out what the actual order would be, from the shortest to the longest perimeter.

Decide as a group which measurement tool to use (string, adding machine tape, or ruler) and which units to use (inches or centimeters). Discuss strategies for measuring the perimeter of the curved figure. If tape or string is used, briefly review how to mark the beginning and end of the length and then measure it. Have volunteers find the perimeter of each shape. Once there is agreement, write the measurements beneath each shape.

What is the actual order of the shapes from shortest perimeter to longest perimeter? How does this compare to your prediction? What advice would you give someone about predicting a shape's perimeter?

Distribute copies of Ordering More Shapes by Perimeter (R29).

⬤ ELL ⬤ **English Language Learners**

Suggest a Sequence Some students may benefit from having a suggested sequence of events for ordering the perimeters. *First,* look at the shapes. *Next,* guess the order of the perimeters from shortest to longest. *Then,* measure the perimeters. *Last,* order the shapes by their actual perimeters.

Additional Resource

Student Math Handbook pages 110–111, 113

Extension

20 MIN   PAIRS

Same Perimeter, Different Shape

Use anytime after Session 1.5.

Math Focus Points

◆ Creating different shapes with the same perimeter

Materials: inch/centimeter rulers (1 per pair), blank paper (1 sheet per pair), R30

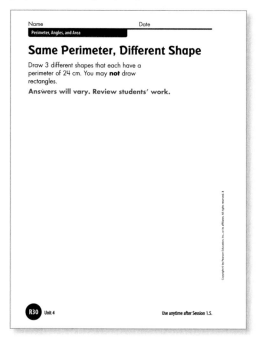

Remind students of Problem 3 on *Student Activity Book* page 10, in which they drew three different rectangles that each had a perimeter of 20 centimeters. Your job today is to draw three shapes *other than rectangles* that all have a perimeter of 10 inches. How can you start? What should you think about as you draw the shapes?

Students might say:

"Think about making a shape where the sides add up to 10. If the first side is 3 inches, I know that I have 7 inches left for the other sides."

Distribute paper and rulers. Have students work in pairs to draw three different shapes other than rectangles with a perimeter of 10 inches.

After students have completed their drawings, ask volunteers to sketch their shapes on the board and label the length of each side.

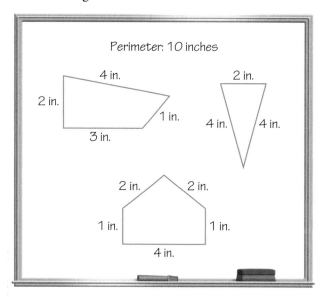

Perimeter: 10 inches

As you were drawing your polygons, what did you have to pay attention to? Have volunteers share their thoughts.

Distribute copies of Same Perimeter, Different Shape (R30).

ELL   English Language Learners

Provide a Word List Write and illustrate the words *ruler, perimeter, inch,* and *centimeter* on chart paper. Hold up a centimeter and inch ruler as you describe the words. Encourage students to use these words as they work with their partners to draw shapes.

Additional Resource

Student Math Handbook page 112

Differentiation in Investigation 2

Mathematics in This Investigation

The mathematics focuses on developing an understanding of area and on using square units to measure the area of regular and irregular shapes.

Understanding the Mathematics

Students plan ahead and visualize the effects of geometric motions (e.g., flips and turns) on shapes to figure out which tetrominoes completely fill a given rectangle. They explain why shapes do or do not work. They make several different shapes with a given area, and they prove that the areas are equivalent. They use rows or columns and counting by groups or multiplication to find the number of squares in a partially covered array. They calculate the area of an irregular shape with a high degree of accuracy, counting parts of squares and combining partial units. They understand area and perimeter, use appropriate labels, and find total measurements efficiently, usually counting by groups.

Option: Assign the Extension activity.

Partially Understanding the Mathematics

Students figure out which tetrominoes completely fill a given rectangle, but may have trouble explaining why shapes do or do not work. They may occasionally think they've found a unique shape because they aren't yet able to fluently visualize the effects of flips and turns. Making more than one shape with a given area, and the idea that different shapes can have the same area, may be challenging. To find the number of squares in a partially covered array, students may sketch the missing squares and then count by groups. They are working to find ways to handle partial units as they calculate the area of an irregular shape. They understand area and perimeter, though they may occasionally forget to label their measurements appropriately.

Option: Assign the Practice activity.

Not Understanding the Mathematics

Students are still developing their understanding of area. They have a hard time seeing how tetrominoes fit together, and they cannot visualize the effects of flips and turns. This means that they mostly guess and check to figure out which tetrominoes completely fill a given rectangle, and their solution may have gaps or overlaps. To find the number of squares in a partially covered array, students may need to recreate the image on graph paper and count by 1s. When finding the area of an irregular shape, they may leave gaps or overlaps between units, and they do not take partial units into account. They may confuse area and perimeter, as well as the units that label each.

Option: Assign the Intervention activity.

Investigation 2 Quiz

In addition to your observations and students' work in Investigation 2, the Quiz (R31) can be used to gather more information.

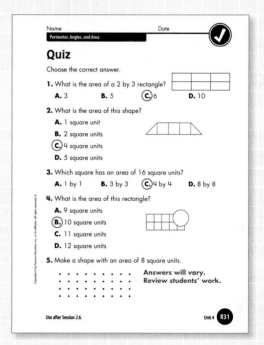

20 MIN **INDIVIDUALS**

Intervention

Two Area Problems

Use anytime after Session 2.4.

Math Focus Points

◆ Finding the area of partially covered rectangles

Vocabulary: area

Materials: construction paper, M19

. . . .

Materials to Prepare: Create two "rugs" by cutting two circles out of construction paper. Draw a 3 by 6 array and a 4 by 4 array on the board. Tape both paper "rugs" on the board so that part of each array is hidden. Make sure that at least one whole row and column in each array is visible.

I've drawn two rectangles, and both are partially covered by a circle. We can imagine that these are tile floors and the circles are rugs.

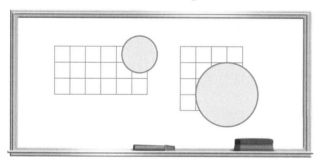

How can we find the area of the first rectangle, even though we can't see every square?

Discuss and try out students' ideas which might include sketching the missing squares on the paper circle. If the idea of using Centimeter Grid Paper (M19) to draw the whole rectangle doesn't come up, bring it up yourself.

Could we use grid paper to draw the rectangle? How would we know how many squares to draw in each row? Be sure to discuss how knowing the number of squares in one row tells you how many squares are in each row. Have students draw the entire rectangle on their grid paper.

After students have finished drawing their rectangles, remove the taped circle from the board. *Does your rectangle have the same number of squares? How did you find the area of the rectangle?*

Students might say:

"I counted the square by 1s."

"I used the rows. 6 + 6 = 12 and 6 more is 18."

Repeat the activity for the 4 by 4 array on the board.

ELL) **English Language Learners**

Model Thinking Aloud Some students will benefit from walking through a problem step-by-step together. Using the first problem, model your thinking aloud. *Part of this rectangle is covered. But, I see 3 rows.* Point to and count the 3 squares in the first column. *I also see 6 columns.* Point to and count the 6 squares in the bottom row. *So I can draw the entire rectangle on my grid paper. Now I can count the squares to find the area.* Model counting by groups and by 1s. *The area is 18 square units.*

Support students in sharing their thinking for these problems.

Additional Resource

Student Math Handbook page 114

Practice

20 MIN   PAIRS

More Perimeter and Area
Use anytime after Session 2.5.

Math Focus Points
◆ Finding the area of an irregular shape
◆ Finding the perimeter of an irregular shape

Materials: 12-inch rulers (1 per pair), string/yarn, color tiles, blank paper (1 sheet per pair), M19, R32

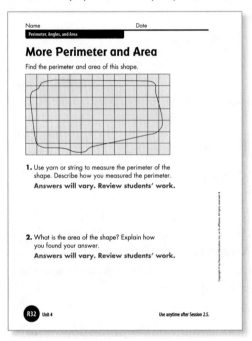

Name _____ Date _____
Perimeter, Angles, and Area

More Perimeter and Area
Find the perimeter and area of this shape.

1. Use yarn or string to measure the perimeter of the shape. Describe how you measured the perimeter.
Answers will vary. Review students' work.

2. What is the area of the shape? Explain how you found your answer.
Answers will vary. Review students' work.

R32 Unit 4   Use anytime after Session 2.5.

Remind students of their work in finding the perimeter and area of their foot in Session 2.5. Today you will find the perimeter and the area of your hand.

Model for students how to trace around your hand on a blank sheet of paper. Keep your fingers together to avoid creating gaps.

Distribute a ruler, string/yarn, and a sheet of blank paper to each pair. Have one partner place their hand, with fingers together, on the piece of paper while the other partner traces around it. Give students time to make their outlines. Then ask a volunteer to explain the strategy they used to find the perimeter of his or her foot.

Students might say:

"I used a piece of yarn to outline my foot. Then I measured the yarn."

How did you find the area of your foot?

Students might say:

"I used color tiles to cover the outline of my foot."

You can use these strategies to find the perimeter and area of your hand or you can try a new one.

Remind students what materials and tools are available: Centimeter Grid Paper (M19), color tiles, yarn/string, and rulers. Give them time to work and then come together to discuss their strategies. Be sure to discuss the units students used and any challenges such as how to measure a curvy line or deal with partial squares.

Distribute copies of More Perimeter and Area (R32).

ELL **English Language Learners**

Provide Sentence Stems Some English Language Learners may have difficulty verbalizing their strategies. Help them by providing sentence stems. For example: First I _____. Then I _____. The perimeter was _____.

Additional Resource

Student Math Handbook pages 113–115

Extension

30 MIN **PAIRS**

Another Perfect Cover-Up
Use anytime after Session 2.2.

Math Focus Points

◆ Understanding that when measuring area, the space being measured must be completely covered with no gaps or overlaps

Vocabulary: tetromino, flip, slide, turn

Materials: tetrominoes (from Session 2.1), connecting cubes, M16 (1 per pair), R33

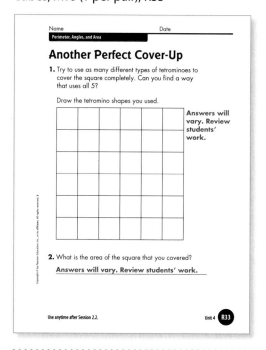

Remind students of *The Perfect Cover-Up*, where they tried to use one tetromino shape to completely cover an 8 × 10 rectangle.

Your job today is to use more than one type of tetromino to completely cover an 8 by 10 rectangle. How might you start?

Students might say:

"I'd try two that seem to fit together. Like maybe the L and the T shapes."

"I think maybe the ones without a part that sticks out might work. I'd try the square and the rectangle."

Distribute an 8 × 10 Rectangle (M16) and connecting cubes to each pair. Work with your partner to completely cover this rectangle with more than one type of tetromino, with no cubes hanging over the sides.

Give pairs time to work, then discuss their arrangements. Which tetrominoes did you try? Did that lead to a perfect fit? What did you find out?

Have volunteers sketch patterns on the board. The pattern below uses the "I" and "square" shapes.

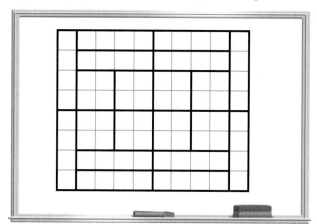

Distribute copies of Another Perfect Cover-Up (R33).

ELL **English Language Learners**

Provide a Word List Hold up a tetromino and use it to illustrate the meaning of words such as *flip, turn,* and *slide.* What does it look like when we flip this tetromino? When we turn it? When we slide it? Have students write each word and draw a picture to help them recall each meaning.

Additional Resource

Student Math Handbook page 116

Differentiation in Investigation 3

Mathematics in This Investigation

The mathematics focuses on the attributes of triangles and quadrilaterals, with a particular focus on right angles.

Understanding the Mathematics

Students build triangles and quadrilaterals according to given constraints, including nonrectangular quadrilaterals. When they draw these shapes, they pay attention to the length of the sides and the size of the angles. They understand that a triangle is a triangle, no matter its orientation. They recognize right angles, as well as angles that are larger than or smaller than 90 degrees.

Option: Assign the **Extension** activity.

Partially Understanding the Mathematics

Students use straws to build a variety of triangles and quadrilaterals, but making shapes that fit particular criteria can be challenging. When drawings those shapes, students often reflect on the overall sense of the shape rather than on estimates of the lengths of the sides and the size of the angles. They know the attributes of triangles, but they may occasionally be thrown off by an irregular triangle or one in an unfamiliar orientation. Similarly, they recognize right angles, but they may not see them in shapes that are oriented unusually (e.g., a square sitting on a vertex rather than on its side).

Option: Assign the **Practice** activity.

Not Understanding the Mathematics

Students build triangles and quadrilaterals though not consistently. They may occasionally make shapes that are not triangles or quadrilaterals because they have trouble keeping all of the attributes in mind at once. Making those shapes according to given constraints is quite challenging, and they may need to trace the results to record them. Students base their thinking about triangles on the overall look of the shape rather than the attributes (e.g., closed figure, straight sides, three sides, three angles, three vertices). They may think a triangle sitting on its base is a triangle while the same triangle, sitting on a vertex, is not. Or they may think a nearly triangular shape with rounded edges or one that is not quite closed, is a triangle. They are not yet thinking about angles as parts of shapes that can be measured.

Option: Assign the **Intervention** activity.

Investigation 3 Quiz

In addition to your observations and students' work in Investigation 3, the Quiz (R34) can be used to gather more information.

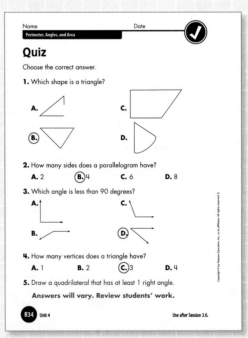

Intervention

20 MIN   INDIVIDUALS

Identifying Triangles

Use anytime after Session 3.2.

Math Focus Points

◆ Identifying the attributes of triangles: three sides, three vertices, and three angles

Vocabulary: triangle, side, vertex (vertices), angle

Materials: straw building kit

Some students do not understand that triangles do not have to have a horizontal base. Work with these students individually. Remind the student of his or her work with the straw building kit to build triangles in Session 3.1.

Today you'll make a triangle the same way you did the other day. Then we'll talk about the triangle you make.

Have the student make a triangle with 3 straws of the same length. If needed, assist the student in using the twist ties and straws.

Let's check to make sure your shape is a triangle. Remind the student of the "Triangles Have . . ." chart made by the class in Session 3.1 (page 108).

Does your shape have three straight sides? Does it have three vertices? Three angles? Is it a triangle?

Typically, students orient their triangle so that the base is horizontal.

Turn the triangle 90 degrees. Is it still a triangle? Does turning the shape change the shape?

Turn the triangle another 90 degrees. Is it still a triangle? Is it still a closed shape with 3 straight sides? Does it still have 3 angles and 3 vertices?

Turn the triangle another 90 degrees. Is it still a triangle?

Throughout your discussion, give the student opportunities to express any reservations. For example: Why doesn't it seem like a triangle to you?

Repeat the above process with triangles made from straws of different lengths.

ELL ▶ **English Language Learners**

Provide a Word List Have students write the words *triangle*, *side*, *vertex*, and *angle* on index cards. Review the meanings and help students draw examples to serve as a reminder of each word's meaning. Post words and illustrations on chart paper for reference.

Additional Resource

Student Math Handbook page 120

Practice

20 MIN   PAIRS

Building Shapes
Use anytime after Session 3.5.

Math Focus Points

◆ Identifying the attributes of triangles: three sides, three vertices, and three angles

◆ Identifying the attributes of quadrilaterals: four sides, four vertices, and four angles

Materials: straw building kits, blank paper, R35

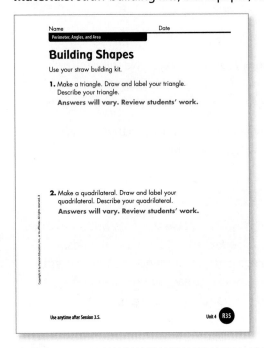

Briefly discuss students' recent work building triangles and quadrilaterals with the straw building kit. What types of triangles and quadrilaterals did you build?

Students might say:

"I made a triangle that had all sides the same length. I made another triangle that had a right angle."

"I made 2 quadrilaterals that had four right angles. One was a rectangle and one was a square."

Write the following directions on the board.

> 1. Make a triangle or a quadrilateral.
> 2. Draw a picture of your shape.
> 3. Write a sentence describing your shape.

Work with your partner. Make a shape and draw a picture of it. Then write a sentence that tells a few facts about your shape. What facts could you include in your description?

Students' responses should include information such as the following:

◆ Is it a triangle or a quadrilateral?

◆ How many sides does it have? How many angles?

◆ What are the lengths of its sides? Are the sides different lengths or are they all equal?

◆ Does it have any right angles?

◆ Are any angles smaller or larger than a right angle?

Give pairs time to work. Ask pairs to sketch their shape on the board, label the lengths of the straws used for each side, and share their written description. Ask other students if there is anything they would add to the description.

Distribute copies of Building Shapes (R35).

ELL English Language Learners

Provide a Word List Have students write *triangle* at the top of an index card, list its attributes, and draw a few examples underneath. Have students do the same for *quadrilateral*. Students can keep the index cards nearby for easy reference.

Additional Resource

Student Math Handbook pages 120–121

Extension

20 MIN   PAIRS

Quadrilaterals with 4 Different Side Lengths

Use anytime after Session 3.3.

Math Focus Points

◆ Identifying the attributes of quadrilaterals: four sides, four vertices, and four angles

◆ Identifying a right angle as having a measure of 90 degrees

Vocabulary: quadrilateral, degree

Materials: straw building kit, blank paper, R36

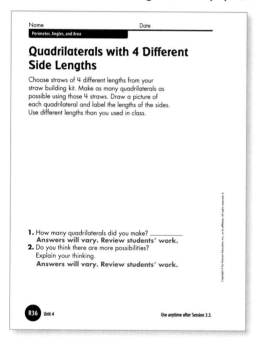

Briefly discuss students' recent work building quadrilaterals with the straw building kit. What is a quadrilateral? How many sides does a quadrilateral have? How many vertices?

Tell students that their job today is to make quadrilaterals whose sides are all different lengths.

Review the length of the straws in the kit: 2 inches, 3 inches, 4 inches, 5 inches, 6 inches, and 8 inches.

So you will choose any four different lengths and use them to make a quadrilateral. Next, draw the quadrilateral and label the lengths of the sides. Model this process for students.

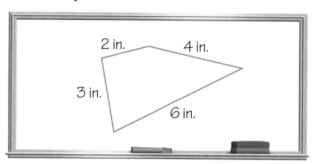

Then give pairs time to work. Challenge students to try to make as many different quadrilaterals as possible from the same four straws. Ask questions to help them think about their quadrilaterals:

◆ What are the lengths of the sides?

◆ How do you know these quadrilaterals are different?

◆ Did you make a rectangle or a square? Why not?

◆ Do any of the quadrilaterals have a right, or 90-degree, angle?

◆ How many quadrilaterals have you made from those four lengths? Do you think you've made *all* the possible quadrilaterals? Why do you think so?

Distribute copies of Quadrilaterals with 4 Different Side Lengths (R36).

ELL English Language Learners

Partner Talk Have pairs describe the features of their quadrilaterals to each other using words such as *side, length, inch, angle,* and *right angle.* Beginner ELLs may need to point to the attributes.

Additional Resource

Student Math Handbook page 121

Unit 5

Differentiation in Investigation 1

Mathematics in This Investigation

The mathematics focuses on developing an understanding of multiplication as combining equal groups. This involves understanding the relationship among repeated addition, skip counting, and multiplication.

Understanding the Mathematics

Students generate many examples of things that come in equal groups. They draw pictures that illustrate situations about equal groups, and they write sentences that describe the important mathematical information—the number of groups, the number of objects in each group, and the total number of objects. They solve problems about such pictures by counting by groups or using a multiplication fact they know, and they use multiplication notation correctly.

Option: Assign the Extension activity.

Partially Understanding the Mathematics

Students generate examples of things that come in equal groups. They draw accurate pictures of multiplication situations, but they may not be able to consistently keep track of each of the pieces of information—the number of groups, the number of objects in each group, and the total number of objects—to write three sentences about each. To solve problems about such pictures, students may use repeated addition or count by groups. They are not yet using multiplication notation correctly.

Option: Assign the Practice activity.

Not Understanding the Mathematics

Students generate a few examples of things that come in equal groups. They have trouble paying attention to all three pieces of information—the number of groups, the number of objects in each group, and the total number of objects—needed to draw a picture and describe it. They may write an expression like "3 + 5" to represent 3 groups with 5 things in each group. To solve problems about equal groups, students draw or model the situation, and count by 1s or add. They do not yet understand how standard notation can be used to represent a situation about equal groups.

Option: Assign the Intervention activity.

Investigation 1 Quiz

In addition to your observations and students' work in Investigation 1, the Quiz (R37) can be used to gather more information.

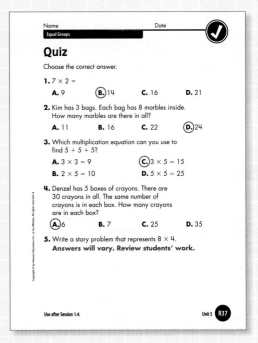

Intervention

25 MIN   PAIRS

Another Picture Problem

Use anytime after Session 1.3.

Math Focus Points

◆ Using and understanding multiplication notation

◆ Writing and solving multiplication problems in context

Materials: blank paper, connecting cubes
(20 per pair)

Some students may need help counting by groups or practice in modeling stories with cubes. Write the following problem on the board and work with students in the area(s) in which they need help.

> Kenji has 3 baskets.
>
> There are 5 apples in each basket.
>
> How many apples are there in all?

Distribute the connecting cubes. Explain that students can use cubes to show the problem.

How could you use the cubes to show the number of apples in 1 basket? How can that help you?

Students might say:

"There are 5 apples in each basket. So I can connect 5 cubes for the first basket, another 5 cubes for the second basket, and another 5 cubes for the third basket."

Have students use cubes to show the problem. Suggest to students that they can add 5s to find the total number of apples because each stick has 5 cubes in it. Then review how to connect repeated addition to multiplication. How many 5s did you add? How can you use multiplication notation to write this?

Pose another problem. This time Kenji has 6 baskets. There are 2 apples in each basket. How many apples are there in all?

Solve the problem. Draw a picture that shows your solution. Then find the answer.

Give students a few minutes to work. I see that you are counting by 1s to find how many apples there are in all. Let's see if there's a faster way to count the number of apples. The problem you are solving is about 6 baskets of apples with 2 apples in each basket. So, what number other than 1 can you count by?

Students might say:

"I can count by 2s because there are 2 apples in each basket."

How many apples are in 2 baskets? What about 3 baskets?

Help students connect skip counting to multiplication. I see that you counted by 2s to find the answer. How many 2s did you count? How could you write this using multiplication notation?

ELL ▶ English Language Learners

Rephrase English Language Learners may struggle with unfamiliar objects in story problems. If possible, share the name of the object in their native language. For example, *manzana* is *apple* in Spanish. It may also help to use classroom objects, such as boxes and cubes, to act out the story with the students.

Additional Resource

Student Math Handbook pages 40–42

Practice

25 MIN   GROUPS

Ears and Toes

Use anytime after Session 1.2.

Math Focus Points

◆ Understanding the relationship among skip counting, repeated addition, and multiplication

◆ Using and understanding multiplication notation

Vocabulary: multiplication, equation

Materials: blank paper, R38

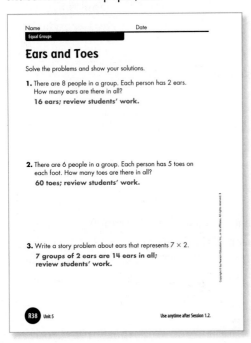

Write the following problem on the board.

> There are 3 people in my group. Each person has 2 ears. How many ears are there in all?
>
> If each person has 5 toes on each foot, how many toes are there in all?

Tell students to solve both problems and show their solutions. When students have finished, ask a few

volunteers to share their pictures. Have each student show a picture and read aloud the equation for the problem. Write some of their examples on the board.

> **3 people with 2 ears each are 6 ears in all**
>
> 2, 4, 6
>
> $2 + 2 + 2 = 6$
>
> $3 \times 2 = 6$
>
> **3 people with 5 toes on each foot are 30 toes in all**
>
> $5 + 5 + 5 + 5 + 5 + 5 = 30$
>
> $6 \times 5 = 30$

Point out how the number of addends or the number of skip counts connects to the groups in the multiplication equations. For example, the three 2s in the addition equation represent the three groups of 2 ears.

If no one mentions it, ask how students could determine the number of toes in all by using groups of 10.

Distribute copies of Ears and Toes (R38).

ELL   English Language Learners

Suggest a Sequence Before students start to work, suggest a sequence of steps to follow:

1. Draw pictures of the groups.

2. Use the groups to write an addition equation.

3. Use the groups to write a multiplication equation.

Additional Resource

Student Math Handbook pages 40–42

Extension

20 MIN **INDIVIDUALS**

How Many in Larger Groups?

Use anytime after Session 1.2.

Math Focus Points

◆ Identifying the number of groups, the number in each group, and the product in a multiplication situation

◆ Using and understanding multiplication notation

Materials: blank paper (3 sheets per student), R39

Name _____ Date _____
Equal Groups

How Many in Larger Groups?

For each problem, write a multiplication equation, solve the problem, and show your solution.

1. In Chiang's picture, there are 8 cartons of eggs. Each carton has 12 eggs. How many eggs are there in all?
Equations will vary. 96 eggs; review students' work.

2. Murphy drew 9 flowers. Each flower has 8 petals. How many petals are there in all?
Equations will vary. 72 petals; review students' work.

3. Elena drew a picture of some stars. Each star has 5 points. There are 55 points in all. How many stars did she draw?
Equations will vary. 11 stars; review students' work.

Use anytime after Session 1.2. Unit 5 **R39**

Briefly discuss students' recent work with pictures of things that come in groups in Session 1.2.

Last time, you were assigned a number, and you chose an item to find how many there were in all. Today, you will choose your own number and write a multiplication equation. It must be greater than 6 and less than 13. It may not be a number you have used before.

Write the following on the board.

> Here are _____.
>
> Each _____ has _____.
>
> There are _____ in all.
>
> Equation: _____

Have students make several different pictures of groups, with each picture showing a different number of groups. Tell students to write the three sentences and multiplication equations for each picture.

What groups did you show? What multiplication equations did you write?

Students might say:

"I drew 7 people with 10 fingers each, and 8 people with 10 toes each. My equations are $7 \times 10 = 70$ and $8 \times 10 = 80$."

Have students find a partner and share their work. Then discuss strategies for finding products and using multiplication notation to show them.

Distribute copies of How Many in Larger Groups? (R39).

ELL **English Language Learners**

Partner Talk Have pairs discuss how their pictures helped them solve the problem. Have more proficient speakers describe their work while less proficient partners point to the relevant parts of the drawing. If both partners are able, have them take turns.

Additional Resource

Student Math Handbook pages 40–41

Differentiation in Investigation 2

Mathematics in This Investigation

The mathematics focuses on skip counting, on finding and using patterns of multiples on 100 charts, and on using skip counting and known combinations to solve multiplication problems.

Additional Resource: *Patterns in the Skip-Counting Charts,* pages 152–153 (See Curriculum Unit 5)

Understanding the Mathematics

Students easily highlight multiples on each 100 chart, and fill in skip-counting circles for those multiples. They can skip count beyond the multiples visible on the 100 chart. They see and use relationships between multiples (e.g., 3 and 6) and between related problems (3 × 4 and 6 × 4). They create representations that illustrate those relationships. Students are gaining fluency with many multiplication combinations, and they use the ones they know to figure out ones they don't know, understanding what has been solved and what remains to be solved.

Option: Assign the Extension activity.

Partially Understanding the Mathematics

Students highlight multiples with ease, but they have to work harder to fill in skip-counting circles for those multiples, particularly beyond 100. They are beginning to understand how making a representation that shows the relationship between two sets of multiples is helpful in using such relationships. Students are gaining fluency with some multiplication combinations, but aren't yet using the ones they know to figure out the ones they don't know.

Option: Assign the Practice activity.

Not Understanding the Mathematics

In order to skip count, particularly past 100, students may have to say each number, emphasizing the multiples of the number by which they are counting (e.g., 1, 2, 3, 4, **5**, 6, 7, 8, 9, **10**, …), or they use objects to model the action of counting by groups. If they see patterns on highlighted 100 charts, they tend to be visual (e.g., "there are two vertical stripes" or "the diagonals are highlighted"). They do not note the mathematical relationships behind those visuals. They may make a representation that shows two related multiplication situations, but they do not really see the relationship. When multiplication combinations arise in their work, they mainly use repeated addition or count by groups to figure out the product. Some students may still count by 1s.

Option: Assign the Intervention activity.

Investigation 2 Quiz

In addition to your observations and students' work in Investigation 2, the Quiz (R40) can be used to gather more information.

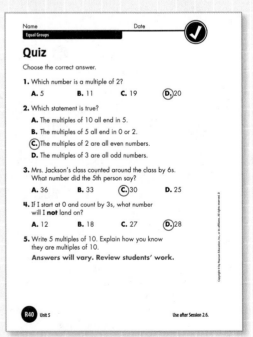

Intervention

30 MIN PAIRS

Skip Counting

Use anytime after Session 2.2.

Math Focus Points

◆ Finding the multiples of the numbers 2, 3, 4, 5, 6, and 10 by skip counting

Materials: lined paper (1 sheet per student), connecting cubes (100 per pair), M2 (optional)

Some students may need help with skip counting. The activities below focus on the multiples of 6 but can be applied to multiples of any number students have studied so far.

First, help students understand what they are doing when they skip count. Distribute the lined paper and cubes to each pair.

Let's show multiples of 6. Make a group of 6 cubes. You have 6 cubes. Write $1 \times 6 = 6$ on the board and have students write it on their sheet of paper. Circle the product. Make another group of 6 cubes. How many cubes do you have now? What equation should you write? Make another group of 6 cubes. What is the total number of cubes you have now? What will you write on your paper?

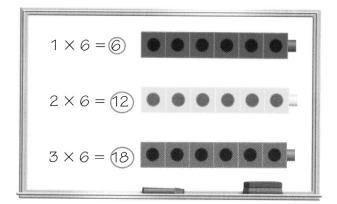

Use the cubes to continue to make and list the multiples of 6 up to 10×6.

Have students work with a partner to check each other's lists.

Count the cubes out loud but softly to check your partner's list. Whisper the numbers between each multiple and then say the multiple—like this: 1, 2, 3, 4, 5, 6, 7, 8, 9, 10, 11, 12, and so on.

Next, have students work with a partner to practice skip counting by 6. Students take turns pointing to the cubes and skip counting to 60 (6, 12, 18, 24...). Each student should have 3–4 opportunities to practice skip counting. Depending on students' level of confidence, consider covering up the equations written on the paper.

If time remains, students should check their work on Multiples of 6 (M2) and make any corrections needed.

Have students find and list the multiples of 6 from 17×6 to 30×6.

ELL English Language Learners

Use Repetition Rather than starting with groups of 6, start with groups of 2. First, talk with students about things that come in 2s, such as eyes, ears, arms, legs, and shoes. Choose a context, such as eyes, and work through the activity making sure to relate the groups to the context. For example, instead of asking how many cubes are in 3 groups of 2, ask how many eyes there would be if there were 3 people. If needed, repeat with another number, such as 5.

Additional Resource

Student Math Handbook pages 42–43

Practice

25 MIN **PAIRS**

Using Known Multiplication Combinations

Use anytime after Session 2.3.

Math Focus Points

◆ Understanding that doubling (or halving) one factor in a multiplication expression doubles (or halves) the product

Materials: R41

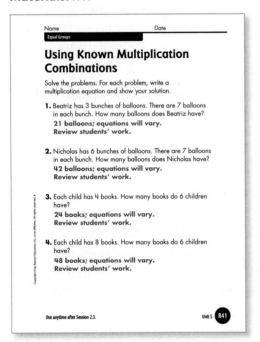

Write the following problems on the board.

> How many wheels do 4 cars have?
>
> How many wheels do 8 cars have?

Work with a partner to solve these problems. Write a multiplication equation for each problem.

Give students a few minutes to work. Then ask for volunteers to share their multiplication equations for each problem.

What combination do you know? How did you use that combination to solve each problem?

Students might say:

"I know that 4 groups of 4 wheels equals 16 wheels. 8 groups is twice as many as 4 groups, so 8 groups have twice as many wheels as 4 groups. 8 groups of 4 wheels equals 32 wheels."

[Gina] says that 8 is twice as large as 4, so the product is twice as large. Now work with your partner to solve another set of problems. Talk about if they are related in this or some other way.

Write the following problems on the board.

> How many sides do 10 quadrilaterals have?
>
> How many sides do 5 quadrilaterals have?

Have students write the multiplication equation for each problem and explain how they figured out each answer. Discuss how the problems are related.

Distribute copies of Using Known Multiplication Combinations (R41).

━━━━ **ELL** ━━━━ **English Language Learners**

Provide a Word List English Language Learners may have difficulty understanding what each problem is asking if they are not familiar with the objects. Write the words *car, wheel, quadrilateral,* and *side* on the board. Discuss the meaning of each, then have students copy each word and draw a picture.

Additional Resource

Student Math Handbook page 44

Extension

25 MIN   PAIRS

Relating Multiples of 3 and 6

Use anytime after Session 2.4.

Math Focus Points

◆ Describing and comparing characteristics of the multiples of a number

◆ Understanding that doubling (or halving) one factor in a multiplication expression doubles (or halves) the product

Materials: students' "Multiples of 3" and "Multiples of 6" charts (from Session 2.2), blank paper, M12 (1 per pair), R42

Name _____ Date _____

Equal Groups

Relating Multiples of 3 and 6

Solve these problems and show your solutions. Use a number line, a 100 chart, or a picture. Use a different way for each problem.

1. 40th multiple of 3

120

40th multiple of 6

240

Review students' work.

2. 60th multiple of 6

360

60th multiple of 3

180

Review students' work.

R42   Unit 5   Use anytime after Session 2.4.

Briefly discuss students' recent work with counting by 3s and 6s and filling bags with 6 apples and then 3 apples.

You found how many apples would be in 30 bags. Today you will find how many apples 50 bags would hold.

Write the following questions on the board.

> What number does the 50th person say when counting by 3s? When counting by 6s?
>
> How many apples will fill 50 bags when filling bags that hold 3 apples? When filling bags that hold 6 apples?

Choose one of these situations. Work with your partner. Use a number line, a 100 chart, or a picture to show your ideas. Use a different way than you used for the 30 groups of 3 and 30 groups of 6. Distribute copies of the 100 Chart with Skip Counting Circles (M12) for students to use, as needed.

Have partners share their solutions. Focus the discussion on how the representations show a relationship between 50 groups of 3 and 50 groups of 6.

Distribute copies of Relating Multiples of 3 and 6 (R42).

ELL ▶ **English Language Learners**

Provide Sentence Stems Some English Language Learners may have difficulty verbalizing the relationship between multiples of 3 and multiples of 6. To help, provide sentence stems. For example:

I have _____ groups of _____.

I have twice as many _____ as _____.

Additional Resource

Student Math Handbook page 44

Differentiation in Investigation 3

Mathematics in This Investigation

The mathematics focuses on understanding arrays as a model for multiplication and on using the arrays to learn the multiplication combinations with products up to 50.

Additional Resources: *Learning Multiplication Combinations*, pages 160–162 (See Curriculum Unit 5); *Count and Compare: A Visual Representation for Multiplication*, pages 97–99 (See *Implementing Investigations in Grade 3*)

Understanding the Mathematics

Students work systematically to find all the ways to represent a number with arrays, using strategies that rely on knowledge about equal groups (e.g., 2 will work for all even numbers), known multiplication combinations, relationships between combinations (e.g., if 2×8 works, then 8×2 does, too), and previously determined arrays. To find the total number of squares in an array, students may "just know" the product. If not, they count by groups or use a combination they do know. They are fluent with all or most of the multiplication combinations, and they use the ones they know to write clues for the ones they don't yet know.

Option: Assign the **Extension** activity.

Partially Understanding the Mathematics

Students find many of the ways to represent a number with arrays, but they may not find all of the possible factor pairs. To find the total number of squares in an array, they count by groups, use multiplication combinations they know, or reflect on other arrays that they know. They are gaining fluency with the multiplication combinations, and they are getting better at using known combinations to figure out ones they don't know.

Option: Assign the **Practice** activity.

Not Understanding the Mathematics

Students find some of the ways to represent a number with arrays, but they work in a more random fashion. When faced with a multiplication combination, or finding the total number of squares in an array, they count by 1s or may be beginning to count by groups.

Option: Assign the **Intervention** activity.

Investigation 3 Quiz

In addition to your observations and students' work in Investigation 3, the Quiz (R43) can be used to gather more information.

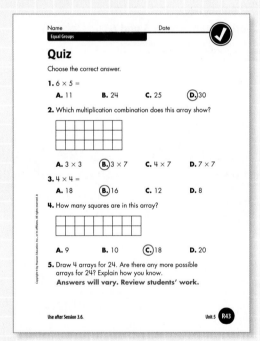

Intervention

20 MIN   **INDIVIDUALS**

Arrays and Skip Counting
Use anytime after Session 3.2.

Math Focus Points

◆ Using arrays to find factors of 2-digit numbers up to 50

Vocabulary: array

Materials: crayons, M20

. . . .

Remind students of the Making Array Cards activity in Session 3.2. I noticed that you counted the squares one by one when you were finding the total number. Let's see if there is a faster way to do that.

Distribute one 4 × 6 array to each student. How many rows are in the array? How many squares are in each row? How can you use skip counting to find the total number of squares?

Students might say:

 "There are 4 rows. There are 6 squares in each row. I can count by 6s four times."

There are 4 groups of 6. Color each group a different color. How many squares are in 1 group? 2 groups? 3 groups? 4 groups?

Draw the grid on the board using a different color for each row. Write the partial totals at the right.

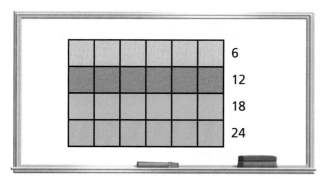

Distribute the other 4 × 6 array to each student.

How many columns are in the array? How many squares are in each column? How can you use skip counting to find the total number of squares?

Students might say:

 "There are 6 columns. There are 4 squares in each column. I can count by 4s six times."

There are 6 groups of 4. Color each group a different color. How many squares are in 1 group? 2 groups? 3 groups? 4 groups? 5 groups? 6 groups?

Draw the grid on the board using a different color for each column. Write the partial totals underneath.

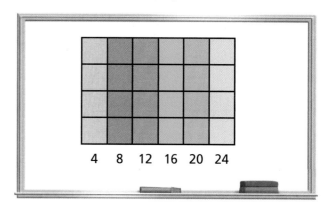

As time allows, repeat the activity with different arrays.

ELL English Language Learners

Provide a Word List English Language Learners often confuse *row* and *column*. Write *row* and *column* on the board and discuss their meanings. Have students write words or draw pictures for each to help them remember the difference. Some beginning ELLs may also confuse *row* with either the act of rowing or roe.

Additional Resource

Student Math Handbook page 49

Practice

20 MIN   GROUPS

How Many Petals?

Use anytime after Session 3.5.

Math Focus Points

◆ Identifying and learning multiplication combinations not yet known

◆ Using known multiplication combinations to determine the product of more difficult combinations

Materials: R44

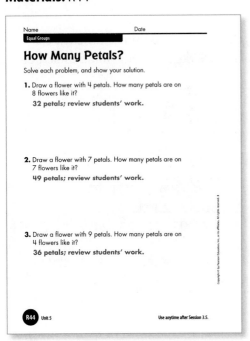

Draw a flower with 7 petals on the board.

This flower has 7 petals. How many petals are on 5 flowers like this one?

Have students work together to solve the problem. What combinations with 5 or 7 as a factor did you use to help you?

Students might say:

"First I solved $5 \times 5 = 25$. Then I solved $5 \times 2 = 10$; $25 + 10 = 35$."

"I thought about the array, 5×7. 4 rows of 7 equal 28. There's 1 more row of 7. So $28 + 7 = 35$."

[Becky] broke 5×7 into $(5 \times 5) + (5 \times 2)$. [Dwayne] broke 5×7 into $(4 \times 7) + (1 \times 7)$. They both used combinations they knew to find the product. What other combinations do you know that can help you solve 5×7?

Now draw a flower with 8 petals on the board.

This flower has 8 petals. How many petals are on 6 flowers like this one? Have students work together to solve the problem. Then have volunteers name known combinations they used to solve it. List the combinations on the board.

Distribute copies of How Many Petals? (R44).

ELL   English Language Learners

Use Repetition Ask each question again using a simpler, shorter form. For example: Seven petals are on 1 flower. How many petals are on 5 flowers?

Additional Resource

Student Math Handbook
Game: *Count and Compare* SMH G9
Materials: Array Cards

Extension

25 MIN **PAIRS**

Arranging More Chairs

Use anytime after Session 3.1.

Math Focus Points

◆ Using arrays to model multiplication situations

Vocabulary: dimension

Materials: connecting cubes (64 per pair), construction paper, scissors, glue sticks, M14 (4 per pair), R45

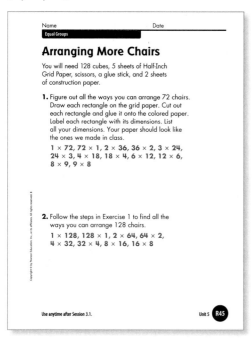

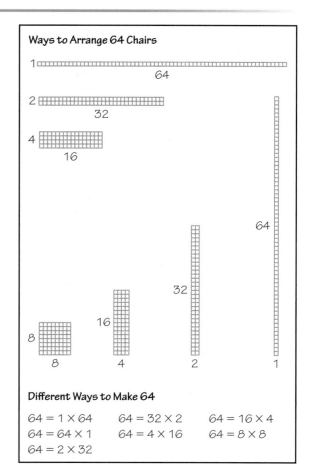

Distribute copies of Arranging More Chairs (R45). Each student will need 128 cubes, 5 copies of M14, scissors, a glue stick, and 2 sheets of construction paper.

Remind students of the Arranging Chairs activity in Session 3.1. Point to some of the posters in the classroom display.

You used cubes to find all the possible ways to arrange a certain number of chairs. Each arrangement was shown as an array.

Distribute the materials. Today you will find all the possible arrangements for 64. Draw each array on Half-Inch Grid Paper (M14). Cut out the arrays, glue them onto a piece of colored paper, and write the title "Ways to Arrange 64 Chairs." Label the dimensions of each array. Students find all the possible arrangements. Then partners share their posters and talk about what they notice.

 ELL **English Language Learners**

Partner Talk Have pairs describe arrangements. More proficient speakers should choose an array and describe the arrangement first. Have less proficient speakers repeat for another array. Then have them work together to discuss similarities and differences between the arrays.

Additional Resource

Student Math Handbook page 45

Differentiation in Investigation 4

Mathematics in This Investigation

The mathematics focuses on developing an understanding of the operation of division and its inverse relationship to multiplication. There is also a focus on developing strategies to solve multiplication and division problems.

Additional Resource: *The Case of Ellen: Deciding When to Nudge,* pages 90–93 (See *Implementing Investigations in Grade 3*)

Understanding the Mathematics

Students use skip counting or known multiplication facts to solve multiplication and division story problems and to play *Missing Factors.* They are comfortable writing both a multiplication and a division problem about the same situation because they understand the relationship between multiplication and division (e.g., seeing that the same problem can be conceptualized as $5 \times ? = 20$ or $20 \div 5 = ?$). They use multiplication and division notation correctly.

Option: Assign the Extension activity.

Partially Understanding the Mathematics

Students use repeated addition, skip counting, or known multiplication facts to solve multiplication and division story problems and to play *Missing Factors.* (At first, students may need to model division situations.) Students are comfortable writing a multiplication problem about a given situation, but they may have to work hard to write a related division problem because keeping track of the parts—a product, one known factor, and one unknown factor—is challenging. They use multiplication notation correctly, though not necessarily for missing-factor problems. They are not yet consistent with division notation.

Option: Assign the Practice activity.

Not Understanding the Mathematics

Students need to model division situations and missing-factor problems, often drawing or using cubes to deal by 1s. They have a stronger ability to recognize, and keep track of, the parts of a multiplication problem—the number of groups, the number in each group, and a product—and use them to write multiplication problems for a given situation. Writing a related division problem, which is dependent on keeping track of the parts—a product, a known factor, and an unknown factor—is very challenging. Students are beginning to use multiplication notation accurately. They do not yet understand how standard notation can be used to represent a missing-factor or division situation.

Option: Assign the Intervention activity.

Investigation 4 Quiz

In addition to your observations and students' work in Investigation 4, the Quiz (R46) can be used to gather more information.

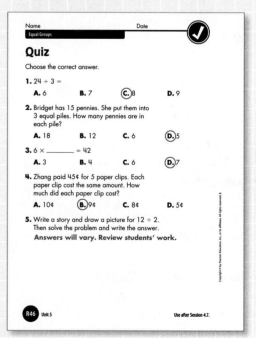

Intervention

25 MIN **INDIVIDUALS**

Modeling Story Problems

Use anytime after Session 4.3.

Math Focus Points

◆ Writing and solving multiplication problems in context

◆ Writing and solving division problems in context

◆ Using and understanding multiplication notation

◆ Using and understanding division notation

Materials: connecting cubes

Discuss the elements of a multiplication story problem. Elicit that two factors are given and that the product is unknown. Then write the following multiplication problem on the board.

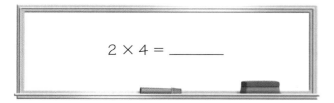

$$2 \times 4 = \underline{\hspace{1cm}}$$

Use your cubes to show what the problem would look like. See if you can think of a situation in which you might have 2 groups of 4 things.

Remind students of the list of "Things That Come in 4s" from Session 1.1 (Investigation 1). What multiplication story problem can you tell using something from that list?

Students might say:

"There are 2 dogs in the yard. Each dog has 4 legs. How many legs are there in all?"

Have students use the cubes to solve his or her problem.

Now discuss the elements of a division story problem. Elicit that the product and one factor are given and that the other factor is unknown.

Write the following division problem on the board.

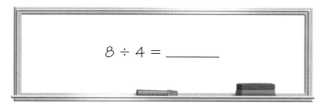

$$8 \div 4 = \underline{\hspace{1cm}}$$

What division story problem about legs of dogs can you tell? Use the cubes to show what the problem would look like.

Students might say:

"There are 8 legs in all. Each dog has 4 legs. How many dogs are there?"

Point out to students that the cubes are already arranged to show the problem. Have the student relate the problem to the groups of cubes and then solve it.

Note that this situation shows 8 things divided into groups of 4. Discuss how $8 \div 4$ can also be represented to show 8 things divided into 4 groups.

If time allows, repeat the activity with 3×6.

ELL **English Language Learners**

Rephrase Review the activity by using simpler language. For example: Write a multiplication problem for 2×4. Write a division problem for $8 \div 4$.

Additional Resource

Student Math Handbook pages 40, 48

Practice

25 MIN   PAIRS

Finding Factors

Use anytime after Session 4.4.

Math Focus Points

◆ Using the inverse relationship between multiplication and division to solve problems

◆ Using and understanding multiplication notation

◆ Using and understanding division notation

Materials: students' multiples charts (from Session 2.1), connecting cubes (50 per group), Array Cards (as needed), R47

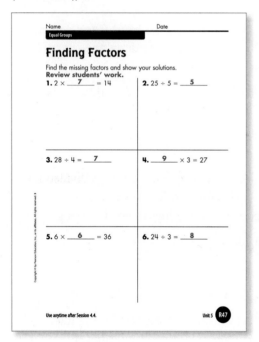

Write the following multiplication problem on the board.

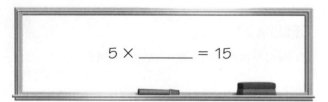
$$5 \times \underline{\hspace{2cm}} = 15$$

Work on your own or with a partner to find the missing factor. Use cubes, a multiples chart, a number line, or array cards. Give students a few minutes to work. Have two or three volunteers share their answers and explain how they approached the

problem. Did anyone use a multiplication fact to find the factor?

Students might say:

 "I know $5 \times 3 = 15$, so the missing factor is 3."

Write the following division problem on the board.

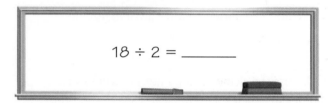
$$18 \div 2 = \underline{\hspace{2cm}}$$

Have students find the missing factor that is the answer in the division equation. Discuss with students the strategies that were used to solve the problem.

Write two more equations with missing factors on the board—one multiplication and one division. Have students find each factor and then share their solutions and strategies.

Distribute copies of Finding Factors (R47).

ELL **English Language Learners**

Model Thinking Aloud Model your thinking as you find each factor. For example, for the multiplication equation you might say: I know the number of *groups*. I know the *total* number of things. I need to find how many are in *each* group. Help students use similar language for the division equation.

Additional Resource

Student Math Handbook
Game: *Missing Factors* SMH G17–G18

Materials: Array Cards, M43

Extension

30 MIN · **INDIVIDUALS**

Problems with Larger Numbers

Use anytime after Session 4.3.

Math Focus Points

◆ Writing and solving multiplication problems in context

◆ Writing and solving division problems in context

Materials: students' multiples charts (from Session 2.1), connecting cubes (50 per group), blank paper (2 sheets per student), Array Cards (as needed), R48

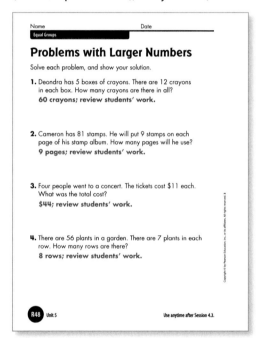

Challenge students who wrote their story problems quickly and easily. Today you'll be writing more problems for the class book. You must use one of the following numbers in each of your problems. Write the following numbers on the board.

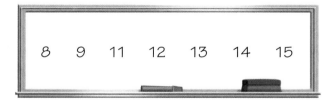

8 9 11 12 13 14 15

What are some story ideas for using these larger numbers?

Students might say:

 "There are 12 things in a dozen. Eggs are sold by the dozen. So one of my stories could be about finding how many eggs are in 3 dozen."

 "There are 9 people in my family. So one of my stories could be about 9 people sharing 72 things equally."

Write two related story problems—one that is about a multiplication situation and one that is about a division situation. Write one story and draw a picture for it on the front of one piece of paper. Solve the problem and write the answer on the back of the paper. Then write and solve the other problem on the other piece of paper.

Collect all the completed stories and add them to the Class Multiplication/Division Book.

Distribute copies of Problems with Larger Numbers (R48).

ELL English Language Learners

Suggest a Sequence Students might need help writing their story problems. You can provide a format for sequencing steps such as the following.

1. Pick a number to use.

2. Write a multiplication problem.

3. Draw a picture.

4. Turn the paper over and solve the problem. A similar sequence of steps can be used for division.

Additional Resource

Student Math Handbook page 48

Differentiation in Investigation 1

Mathematics in This Investigation

The mathematics focuses on interpreting, describing, and making graphs that show temperature over time.

Additional Resource: *Using Line Graphs to Represent Change,* pages 117–118 (See Curriculum Unit 6)

Understanding the Mathematics

Students easily identify high and low temperatures, as well as the corresponding dates and cities, on graphs that show change over time. They accurately estimate temperatures that are not specified on the graph and efficiently find the difference between two temperatures, even when one is a negative number. Students create accurate graphs of given data, match graphs to stories, and write stories to match graphs.

Option: Assign the Extension activity.

Partially Understanding the Mathematics

Students identify high and low temperatures on graphs that show change over time, but they may have to work to relate them to the dates and cities connected to those temperatures. Students are developing strategies for more accurately estimating temperatures that are not specified on the graph. They find the difference between two temperatures, though negative numbers present a challenge. Students can create graphs for given data, but they need practice to do so accurately and efficiently. They can connect stories and graphs, but may at times focus on only one feature of a story or graph, rather than looking at the overall story or shape of the data.

Option: Assign the Practice activity.

Not Understanding the Mathematics

Students find it quite challenging to identify high and low temperatures on graphs that show change over time and relate those temperatures to dates and cities. Students may have a hard time determining a temperature when it is not specified by the graph. They find the difference between two temperatures, but they use inefficient strategies that involve many steps, which can result in errors. Creating an accurate graph from given data is difficult. Students have trouble connecting descriptions of temperatures to feature of graphs, and vice versa.

Option: Assign the Intervention activity.

Investigation 1 Quiz

In addition to your observations and students' work in Investigation 1, the Quiz (R49) can be used to gather more information.

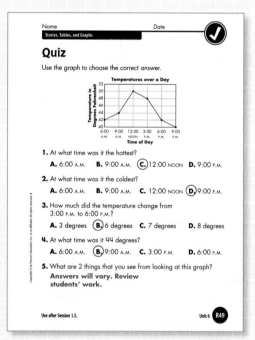

Intervention

25 MIN INDIVIDUALS

Points on a Graph

Use anytime after Session 1.1.

Math Focus Points

◆ Reading and interpreting temperatures on a line graph

Vocabulary: temperature, degrees

Materials: *Student Activity Book* p. 1

. . . .

Have students look at *Student Activity Book* page 1. What information is given at the top of the graph? The left side? The bottom? How do we know which city the points on the graph are showing?

Inform students they are going to be looking at the temperatures for the North Pole.

Ask students to point to September 1. Which temperature is for the North Pole? Slide your finger up the line for September 1 until you reach the temperature for the North Pole. What was the temperature? How do you know?

Students might say:

"I stopped at the square that's the North Pole. The temperature was 30 degrees."

Ask students to point to September 22 and repeat the procedure. Slide your finger up the line until you find the temperature for the North Pole. What do you think the temperature is? Students might need support in determining that the line between 10 and 20 represents 15 degrees, and the temperature is slightly above that.

Students might say:

"It's a little bit above 15 degrees because the line on the graph isn't going through the square. So maybe 17 degrees?"

Now demonstrate the opposite activity. Let's find when the temperature at the North Pole was 0 degrees. Find 0 at the left of the graph. Slide your finger to the right until you find a square to show the North Pole temperature. Slide your finger down and read the date. What date was it?

As time allows, repeat with other dates and temperatures.

ELL English Language Learners

Provide Sentence Stems Some English Language Learners may have difficulty reading information on a line plot and reporting their findings. To help them organize their information, provide sentence stems such as the following.

The location is _____.

The date is _____.

The temperature is _____.

Additional Resource

Student Math Handbook pages 69–70

Practice

20 MIN   PAIRS

Another Temperature Graph
Use anytime after Session 1.3.

Math Focus Points

◆ Describing the overall shape of a line graph—increasing, decreasing, staying the same

◆ Finding the difference between values on a line graph, including the difference between a positive and negative value

Materials: M14 (1 per pair), R50

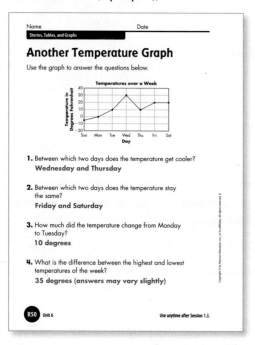

Materials to Prepare: Plot the points shown below on Temperatures over a Day Graph (M14) and give one copy to each pair of students.

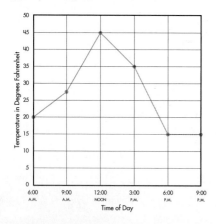

Today you will look at another temperature graph. Study the graph and talk about it with your partner.

Elicit information about temperature changes by asking questions such as the following:

◆ Which parts of the graph show the temperature rising?

◆ Which parts of the graph show the temperature dropping?

◆ Does any part of the graph show that the temperature is staying the same? How do you know?

Have students calculate differences between temperatures by asking questions such as:

◆ How much did the temperature change from 12:00 noon to 3:00 P.M.?

◆ What is the difference between the highest and lowest temperatures of the day?

Accept reasonable estimates for points that fall between marked values.

Distribute copies of Another Temperature Graph (R50).

ELL English Language Learners

Model Thinking Aloud Using the graph, model your thinking for answering the last question aloud. I want to find the difference between the highest temperature and the lowest temperature. The highest temperature is 45 degrees. The lowest temperature is 15 degrees. 45 − 15 is 30, so the difference between the highest and lowest temperature is 30 degrees.

Additional Resource

Student Math Handbook page 72

Extension

20 MIN   PAIRS

What Would You Wear?

Use anytime after Session 1.2.

Math Focus Points

◆ Associating a story with its corresponding graph

Materials: blank paper, T75, R51

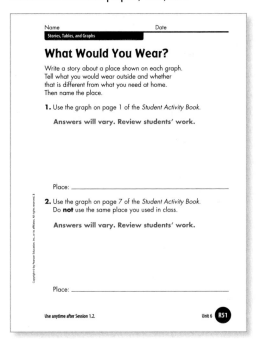

Display Temperatures over a Year Graph (T75). Then tell the following story.

I have picked a place shown on the graph. I am imagining that I will live there for 1 year. I would want to wear leggings, a heavy coat with a hood, double-thick socks, a scarf, and gloves outside. It is different from what I need at home because the temperature at home is warmer than [the same as; colder than] this place. Which place did I pick? How do you know?

Students might say:

"You picked Churchill, Canada. I know because your clothing is for cold outdoor temperatures, and most of the year the temperature in Churchill, Canada, is below freezing."

Write the following starter sentences on the board.

> I have picked a place on the graph. I am imagining that I will live there for 1 year. I would want to wear . . .

Distribute the blank paper. Have students write their own story about one of the places on the graph, using the sentences on the board as the start to the story. Tell students to include what they would wear outside and whether or not that is different from what they would need at home. Students may choose to illustrate their stories with people wearing the clothing described in the story.

Give students time to write their stories. Then have partners swap papers and identify the location described.

Distribute copies of What Would You Wear? (R51).

ELL   English Language Learners

Provide a Word List English Language Learners may be unfamiliar with the names for some items of clothing. Prior to beginning the activity, have students work together to form a list of cold-weather and warm-weather clothing items. Allow students to illustrate the items of clothing, if desired. Keep the list posted during the activity.

Additional Resource

Student Math Handbook pages 67, 71

Differentiation in Investigation 2

Mathematics in This Investigation

The mathematics focuses on constructing, describing, and extending number sequences with constant increments.

Additional Resource: *Repeating Patterns and Counting Numbers,* pages 124–125 (See Curriculum Unit 6)

Understanding the Mathematics

Students use knowledge about multiplication and multiples of 3 to figure out the color of particular cubes in an ABC pattern. They are comfortable with the multiples of 3, and they can count by 3s starting at 1, 2 or 3. They use work they've already done (e.g., the numbers associated with the green cubes) to solve related problems.

Option: Assign the Extension activity.

Partially Understanding the Mathematics

Students skip count by 3s to figure out the color of particular cubes in an ABC pattern, perhaps using their highlighted 100 charts to help them. They are comfortable counting by 3s when they start with 3, but are not yet fluent when starting with 1 or 2. Particularly at first, they may treat each question as a new and unrelated problem, rather than connect it to the work they've already done (e.g., the numbers associated with the green cubes).

Option: Assign the Practice activity.

Not Understanding the Mathematics

Students figure out the color of particular cubes in an ABC pattern by extending the pattern and counting. They are just developing fluency with counting by 3s and may need to quietly say the in-between numbers if they start counting from 1 or 2. Students don't see connections between the numbers generated by the different colors in an ABC pattern. They also don't see how connecting the numbers and the colors in the pattern could help them solve problems about cubes farther along in the pattern. They may incorrectly assume that the blue cubes are multiples of 2 because the greens are multiples of 3.

Option: Assign the Intervention activity.

Investigation 2 Quiz

In addition to your observations and students' work in Investigation 2, the Quiz (R52) can be used to gather more information.

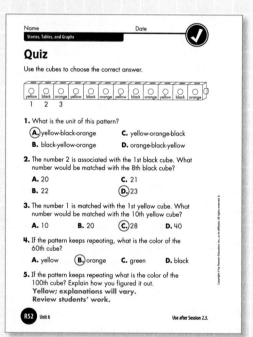

Intervention

20 MIN **PAIRS**

Where Are the Black Cubes?

Use anytime after Session 2.2.

Math Focus Points

◆ Associating counting numbers with elements of a pattern

◆ Describing and extending a number sequence with a constant increment (e.g., 3, 6, 9, … or 2, 5, 8, …)

Vocabulary: repeating pattern, unit

Materials: connecting cubes (4 yellow, 4 black, and 4 orange per student), blank paper

Prepare a 12-cube train with a repeating yellow-black-orange pattern.

Show students the pattern. This is a repeating pattern. What is the unit of this pattern? How many cubes are there in the part that repeats over and over?

Distribute connecting cubes and paper to each student. Build a train of 12 cubes with the same yellow-black-orange pattern. Then put your cube train on the paper.

If we count these cubes 1, 2, 3, 4, and so on, what number is matched with the 1st black cube? Write a 2 under the 1st black cube. What number is matched with the 2nd black cube? Write a 5 under the 2nd black cube. What about the 3rd black cube? Write an 8 under it. What about the 4th black cube? Write an 11 under it.

What are the numbers for the first 4 black cubes? What do you know about these numbers?

Students might say:

"2, 5, 8, 11. The numbers are getting bigger."

Now work with your partner to find the numbers for the first 10 black cubes. Students may need additional cubes, or want to draw the cubes on their paper. When students have found all the numbers, ask for the list and write it on the board.

2, 5, 8, 11, 14, 17, 20, 23, 26, 29

What do you notice about this list of numbers for the black cubes?

Students might say:

"Each number is 3 more than the number before it."

ELL **English Language Learners**

Partner Talk Write the ordinal numbers for 1st to 10th on the board and review them with students. Pair students with different levels of language proficiency. Have them work together to name the position of each cube. Then have one partner choose a position while the other finds the cube in that position. Have them switch roles and repeat as needed.

Additional Resource

Student Math Handbook pages 73–74

Practice

20 MIN **PAIRS**

More Repeating Patterns
Use anytime after Session 2.2.

Math Focus Points

◆ Associating counting numbers with elements of a pattern

◆ Describing and extending a number sequence with a constant increment (e.g., 3, 6, 9, ... or 2, 5, 8, ...)

Vocabulary: unit, repeating pattern, multiple

Materials: blank paper (1 sheet per pair), R53

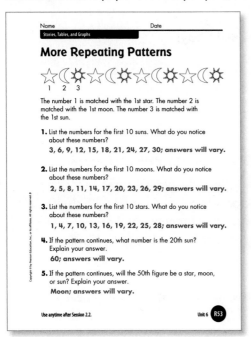

Name _____ Date _____
Stories, Tables, and Graphs

More Repeating Patterns

1 2 3

The number 1 is matched with the 1st star. The number 2 is matched with the 1st moon. The number 3 is matched with the 1st sun.

1. List the numbers for the first 10 suns. What do you notice about these numbers?
3, 6, 9, 12, 15, 18, 21, 24, 27, 30; answers will vary.

2. List the numbers for the first 10 moons. What do you notice about these numbers?
2, 5, 8, 11, 14, 17, 20, 23, 26, 29; answers will vary.

3. List the numbers for the first 10 stars. What do you notice about these numbers?
1, 4, 7, 10, 13, 16, 19, 22, 25, 28; answers will vary.

4. If the pattern continues, what number is the 20th sun? Explain your answer.
60; answers will vary.

5. If the pattern continues, will the 50th figure be a star, moon, or sun? Explain your answer.
Moon; answers will vary.

Use anytime after Session 2.2.   Unit 6 **R53**

Draw a square-triangle-circle pattern on the board.

1 2 3

How is this pattern like the red-blue-green cube train pattern? What is the unit in this pattern?

Students should mention that it is a repeating pattern with 3 shapes in the part that repeats over and over. The unit is square-triangle-circle.

If we count the shapes 1, 2, 3, 4, and so on, as we did with the cubes, what number is matched with the 1st circle? What about the 2nd circle? Find the numbers for the first 10 circles.

Ask for a volunteer to read the list. How did you get the numbers for the circles?

Students might say:

"Skip count by 3s. All the numbers are multiples of 3."

Now find the numbers for the first 10 triangles and the first 10 squares. How can you use what you know about the circles to help you with the triangles and squares?

Students might say:

"The number for a triangle is one less than the number for a circle. The number for a square is one more than the number for a circle."

Collect the list of numbers for the triangles and squares. Discuss students' strategies for finding them.

Distribute copies of More Repeating Patterns (R53).

ELL **English Language Learners**

Provide a Word List Write the list of cardinal numbers and their related ordinal numbers from 1st to 10th on the board. Read through the list. Then, point to various ordinal numbers and have students practice saying the name of the position aloud.

Additional Resource

Student Math Handbook page 74

Extension

20 MIN

PAIRS

What Is It?

Use anytime after Session 2.3.

Math Focus Points

◆ Determining the element of an ABC pattern associated with a particular counting number

◆ Identifying numbers that are multiples of 3, or 1 less or 1 more than a multiple of 3

Vocabulary: unit, repeating pattern, multiple

Materials: blank paper (1 sheet per pair), R54

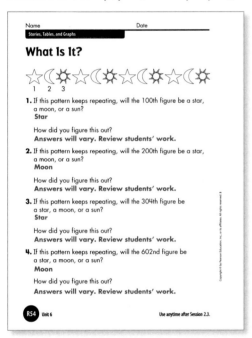

Draw a square-triangle-circle pattern on the board.

Here is a shape pattern with 12 shapes. How is this pattern like the red-blue-green cube train pattern? What is the unit of this pattern? What do you know about the numbers for all of the circles?

Students should mention that it is a repeating pattern with a unit of square-triangle-circle. The circles are in the same position as the green cubes, so, as with the green cubes, all of the numbers for the circles are multiples of 3.

If the pattern keeps repeating, what shape is the 121st shape? Work with your partner to figure it out. You may not count by ones.

Ask volunteers to share their methods for finding the 121st shape.

Students might say:

"I know that 120 is a multiple of 3, so the 120th shape is a circle. The 121st shape is 1 shape after a circle. That's a square."

Now work together to find the 299th shape in the pattern. Remember, you may not count by ones. Ask volunteers to share their methods for finding the 299th shape.

Students might say:

"I know that 300 is a multiple of 3, so the 300th shape is a circle. The 299th shape is 1 shape before a circle. That's a triangle."

Distribute copies of What Is It? (R54).

ELL **English Language Learners**

Rephrase Some students may have difficulty with the word *unit*. The *unit* is the part of the pattern that *repeats* over and over. Point to each shape in the pattern on the board. The pattern on the board is square, triangle, circle. After the circle, the pattern starts again: square, triangle, circle. Have students draw a repeating pattern and circle the unit.

Additional Resource

Student Math Handbook pages 73–74

Differentiation in Investigation 3

Mathematics in This Investigation

The mathematics focuses on using tables and graphs to represent and compare situations with constant rates of change.

Additional Resource: *Graphs of Situations with a Constant Rate of Change,* pages 130–133 (See Curriculum Unit 6)

Understanding the Mathematics

Students make representations that clearly show the number of marbles at the beginning, the number gained each night, and the total each day. When given data about other marble situations, students find a rule that allows them to compute the number of marbles on Day 5 and on Day 10 without solving for the intervening days. They compare situations where the starting amounts are different but the nightly increase is the same, and situations where the starting amounts are the same and the increase is different, using words like *faster, slower, steeper,* and *the same.* They make graphs of data presented in tables, understand the meaning of each point, and interpret the overall meaning of the graph.

Option: Assign the **Extension** activity.

Partially Understanding the Mathematics

Students make representations that are fairly clear. When given data about other marble situations, they may compute the number of marbles for each day, but over time they begin to look for more general rules. When comparing two sets of data, students may focus more on patterns in one set (e.g., Tovar's marbles grow by 10 each day), or they may focus on comparing only the number of marbles on a particular day (e.g., on Day 10 Tovar has 40 and Zupin has 80). They work hard to graph data presented in tables and to understand the meaning of each point. Their ability to describe what one graph shows is developing, but comparing two graphs is a challenge.

Option: Assign the **Practice** activity.

Not Understanding the Mathematics

Students make representations that show most of the data about marble situations, but it is likely not clear to others. When given data about other marble situations, they compute the number of marbles for each day. They are just learning to describe one set of data, and may focus on particular aspects (e.g., on Day 10 Tovar has 10), rather than the overall story told by the data. Comparing two sets is difficult. Graphing data presented in tables is challenging, and students often lose sight of the meaning of each point.

Option: Assign the **Intervention** activity.

Investigation 3 Quiz

In addition to your observations and students' work in Investigation 3, the Quiz (R55) can be used to gather more information.

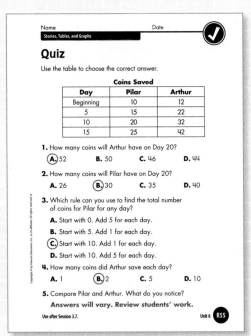

Intervention

20 MIN   INDIVIDUALS

Comparing Data on Two Graphs

Use anytime after Session 3.5.

Math Focus Points

◆ Comparing situations by describing differences in their graphs

Vocabulary: horizontal axis, vertical axis

Materials: chart paper

....

Materials to Prepare: Copy the graphs below onto chart paper and display for students.

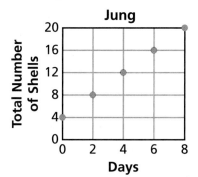

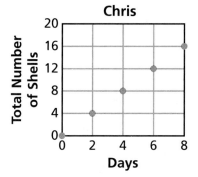

Jung and Chris are both collecting shells. The graph at the top shows Jung's shells, and the graph at the bottom shows Chris's shells.

Review the parts of a graph. What do the numbers along the horizontal axis show? What do the numbers along the vertical axis show? Are the numbers the same on both graphs?

Discuss the points on Jung's graph. Each point shows how many shells Jung had on a certain day. How many shells did Jung start with? Which point shows that? How many shells did she have on Day 2? Day 4? Day 6? Day 8? How many shells did Jung collect each day? How do you know she collected 2 shells each day?

Have a similar discussion of the points on Chris's graph. Then use the two graphs to compare the shell accumulations. How is Chris's graph the same as Jung's graph? How is it different?

Students might say:

 "They both collected 2 shells each day. Jung started with 4 shells, but Chris started with 0 shells."

If Chris and Jung keep collecting 2 shells each day, will they ever have the same number of shells on the same day? How does the graph show that?

Have students find partners to discuss their answers. Elicit that Jung will always have 4 more shells than Chris. Points for the same day show that Jung's total is always 4 more than Chris's total.

ELL ⟩ **English Language Learners**

Provide a Word List Write the words *horizontal axis* and *vertical axis* on the board. Some English Language Learners may be familiar with the word *horizon*. If so, that may help them remember that *horizontal* is side-to-side rather than top-to-bottom. Explain the difference between *horizontal* and *vertical* and have students draw pictures.

Additional Resource

Student Math Handbook pages 81–82

Practice

25 MIN **GROUPS**

Plotting Points on a Graph

Use anytime after Session 3.4.

Math Focus Points

◆ Plotting points on a graph to represent a situation in which one quantity is changing in relation to another

Materials: chart paper, 2 markers of different colors, R56

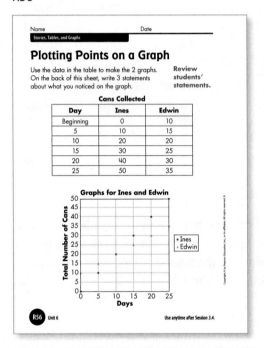

Materials to Prepare: Copy the Becky and Kenji graph shown in the right-hand column (but not the data on the graph) onto chart paper. Reproduce the following table on the board.

Day	Becky	Kenji
Beginning	5	5
5	10	15
10	15	25
15	20	35

Becky and Kenji are collecting cans for recycling. Let's make a graph to show the data in the table.

Display the graph you prepared earlier.

Let's look at the data for Becky. How many cans is Becky beginning with? How do we plot that point on the graph?

Have a volunteer come to the board to plot the point. Then repeat the process for plotting the remainder of points for Becky. Use the same color marker for all of Becky's points.

Now let's plot Kenji's points. Discuss how to plot these points. Have volunteers use a marker in a second color to plot them. The completed graph should look like the one below.

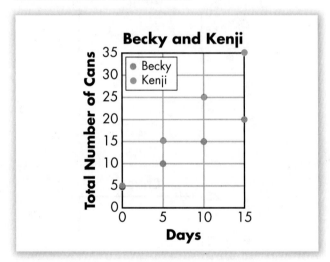

Discuss the graphs. Have students tell what they notice about Becky's graph, what they notice about Kenji's graph, and how they are different.

Distribute copies of Plotting Points on a Graph (R56).

Model Thinking Aloud Model how to verbalize information about a point on the graph. For example: This point shows that Becky has 15 cans on Day 10. Indicate another point and have students use similar language to tell a statement about it.

Additional Resource

Student Math Handbook pages 79–82

Extension

20 MIN   PAIRS

Finding a Rule

Use anytime after Session 3.3.

Math Focus Points

◆ Making rules that relate one variable to the other in situations with a constant rate of change

Materials: blank paper (1 sheet per pair), calculators (1 per pair), R57

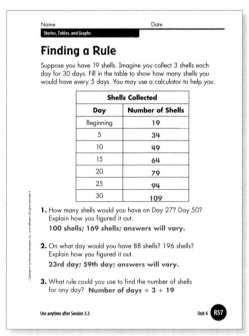

Name _____ Date _____

Stories, Tables, and Graphs

Finding a Rule

Suppose you have 19 shells. Imagine you collect 3 shells each day for 30 days. Fill in the table to show how many shells you would have every 5 days. You may use a calculator to help you.

Shells Collected	
Day	**Number of Shells**
Beginning	19
5	34
10	49
15	64
20	79
25	94
30	109

1. How many shells would you have on Day 27? Day 50? Explain how you figured it out.
100 shells; 169 shells; answers will vary.

2. On what day would you have 88 shells? 196 shells? Explain how you figured it out.
23rd day; 59th day; answers will vary.

3. What rule could you use to find the number of shells for any day? **Number of days × 3 + 19**

Use anytime after Session 3.3.   Unit 6 **R57**

. . . .

Materials to Prepare: Write the following sentences and data table on the board.

> Keisha has 38 pennies. She wants to save 6 pennies a day for 30 days.
>
> | Day | Keisha |
> | --- | --- |
> | Beginning | |
> | 5 | |
> | 10 | |
> | 15 | |
> | 20 | |
> | 25 | |
> | 30 | |

Work with your partner. Copy the table on your paper and then fill it in. If you want, you may use your calculator. Discuss the methods students used to complete the table.

How many pennies does Keisha save every 5 days? How do you know?

Students might say:

"She saves 6 pennies a day, so 5 times 6 gives 30 pennies for all 5 days."

Fill in the table on the board with the students. (*38, 68, 98, 128, 158, 188, 218*) Then have students explain how they completed the table.

How many pennies would Keisha have on Day 9? Day 17? Day 32? (*92 on Day 9; 140 on Day 17; 230 on Day 32*) What rule can you use to find the total number of pennies for any day?

Students might say:

"Multiply the number of days by 6. Then add the 38 pennies that Keisha started with."

Distribute copies of Finding a Rule (R57).

ELL **English Language Learners**

Provide Sentence Stems Have partners take turns explaining how to find the number of pennies for days that are and are not listed on the table. Have students use complete sentences to give the answers. Provide the following sentence stem:
Keisha had _____ pennies on Day _____.

Additional Resource

Student Math Handbook page 87

Differentiation in Investigation 1

Mathematics in This Investigation

The mathematics focuses on developing an understanding of the meaning of fractions as equal parts of a whole or a group.

Additional Resource: *Using Representations in Brownie Problems: What Do You Call a Third of a Half?*, pages 99–102 (See *Implementing Investigations in Grade 3*)

Understanding the Mathematics

Students understand fractions as equal parts of a whole and use their understanding to share one or more brownies among different numbers of people. They make accurate representations of fractions, often using one fraction (e.g., thirds) to help with another (e.g., sixths). They use such reasoning to prove that different-looking pieces can be equal or to order fractions. They combine like and unlike fractions (e.g., $\frac{1}{2} + \frac{1}{4} + \frac{1}{8} + \frac{1}{8}$) to make a whole, and use fraction notation accurately. Students understand that the larger the denominator, the smaller the fraction, because the whole has been cut into more pieces, resulting in pieces that are smaller. They solve problems about fractions of sets efficiently.

Option: Assign the **Extension** activity.

Partially Understanding the Mathematics

Students understand fractions as equal parts of a whole, but they may at first be surprised that those parts can look different. They use strategies like folding, measuring, and cutting to make fractional pieces and to solve problems that involve sharing one or more brownies among a group. At first, students may not see relationships among different fractions (e.g., halves and fourths). They combine like fractions to make a whole (e.g., $\frac{3}{4} + \frac{1}{4}$), but they may find combining like and unlike fractions (e.g., $\frac{1}{2} + \frac{1}{4} + \frac{1}{4}$) challenging at first. They are not yet consistently using notation accurately.

Option: Assign the **Practice** activity.

Not Understanding the Mathematics

Students are still developing an understanding of fractions as equal parts of a whole. They may think that any whole with 3 parts represents thirds, regardless of the size of the pieces. They may not see how different-looking pieces can represent the same fraction of a whole. Making accurate representations of fractions is challenging for these students. Their strategies for sharing brownies among one or more people involve directly modeling the problem. Using notation to name the resulting amount is difficult. To make a whole, they rely mainly on combining unit fractions with the same denominator (e.g., $\frac{1}{4} + \frac{1}{4} + \frac{1}{4} + \frac{1}{4}$).

Option: Assign the **Intervention** activity.

Investigation 1 Quiz

In addition to your observations and students' work in Investigation 1, the Quiz (R58) can be used to gather more information.

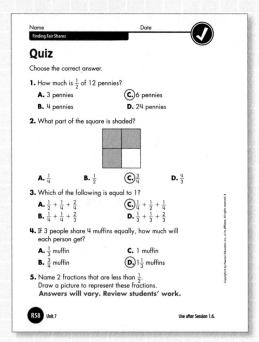

Intervention

20 MIN   INDIVIDUALS

Sharing Five Brownies

Use anytime after Session 1.5.

Math Focus Points

◆ Dividing a group into equal parts and naming the parts with fractions

◆ Using mixed numbers to represent quantities greater than 1

Materials: scissors, construction paper (3 sheets per student), M11

. . . .

Distribute scissors, construction paper, and Small Brownies (M11) to each student. Have students cut apart the brownies on M11.

Explain that today they will be sharing brownies among several people. Have each student write the name of one person at the top of each piece of construction paper. Briefly review some basic problems.

Suppose 2 people were sharing 2 brownies. How much would each person get? What about 4 brownies? What if 2 people shared 1 brownie? Demonstrate how to cut one brownie into halves.

Imagine you have 5 brownies to share equally among 2 people. How can you start to share the brownies equally?

Students might say:

"Give out whole brownies to each person. Then share the extra brownie."

Let's start by giving out whole brownies to each person. How many whole brownies does each person get? How many brownies do you still need to share? What can you do now? Remember, each person needs to have the same amount of brownies.

Elicit that the remaining brownie can be cut in half. Have students do this and distribute the halves.

Have you used up all 5 brownies? Did everyone get an equal portion? How much did each person get? *($2\frac{1}{2}$ brownies)*

Have the students check that all the pieces add up to 5 brownies.

Next, pose a problem for students to work on independently. This time, 3 people are going to share 7 brownies. How many brownies will each person get? Remind students to set aside the halves from the previous problem and take 7 whole small brownie squares to begin with. As students are working, notice in particular if they cut a single brownie into 3 *equal* pieces and whether or not they label it as $\frac{1}{3}$. Discuss students' strategies for sharing the brownies. Confirm that each person gets $2\frac{1}{3}$ brownies, then have the students reassemble the pieces and confirm that there are 7 whole brownies.

Pose additional brownie problems that require students to work with halves and thirds, such as 7 brownies/2 people or 8 brownies/3 people. Students can also work with fourths as they share 5 brownies among 4 people.

ELL   English Language Learners

Suggest a Sequence Some English Language Learners may need guidance understanding the process for sharing the brownies. Provide them with a sequence of steps, such as the following.

1. Cut the brownies into equal parts.

2. Share the parts equally until they are gone.

3. Write the fraction that shows how many pieces each person gets.

Additional Resource

Student Math Handbook pages 61–62

Practice

20 MIN PAIRS

More Sharing Problems
Use anytime after Session 1.6.

Math Focus Points

◆ Dividing a group into equal parts and naming the parts with fractions

◆ Naming fractional parts with fractions that have numerators greater than 1 ($\frac{3}{4}$, $\frac{2}{3}$, $\frac{3}{6}$, etc.)

Materials: connecting cubes (20 per pair), blank paper, M11 (1 per pair), R59

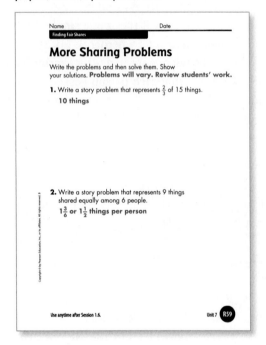

Write the following on the board.

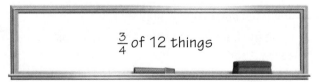

$$\frac{3}{4} \text{ of } 12 \text{ things}$$

Can you tell me a story about $\frac{3}{4}$ of 12 things?

Collect a few examples. Then have students write their story at the top of the paper and work with a partner to solve it. Tell students to use cubes, brownies, or pictures to show the solution. How did you figure out what $\frac{3}{4}$ of 12 is?

Students might say:

 "I put 12 cubes into 4 equal groups of 3. I took 3 out of the 4 groups. That's 3 plus 3 plus 3, which is 9."

 "I cut 12 brownies into fourths. I took away $\frac{1}{4}$ from each brownie. That gave me a total of 36 fourths, which is 9 whole brownies."

Write the following on the board.

5 things shared equally among 3 people

Have volunteers suggest story scenarios. Be sure that they suggest items that can be cut (muffins, apples, bananas, brownies, granola bars, etc). Then have partners write and solve the problem on the back of their papers.

How did you share 5 things equally among 3 people?

Distribute copies of More Sharing Problems (R59).

ELL English Language Learners

Provide a Word List Write the words *group*, *share*, and *equal parts* on the board. Discuss the meaning of each with students. Then, have students act out a situation where a group of students share equal parts.

Additional Resource
Student Math Handbook pages 61–62

20 MIN   PAIRS

Extension

A Sharing Challenge
Use anytime after Session 1.5.

Math Focus Points

◆ Dividing a group into equal parts and naming the parts with fractions

Materials: blank paper (1 sheet per pair), M11 (1 per pair), R60

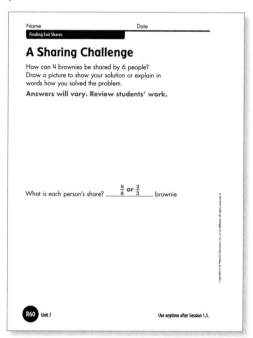

- -

Write the following on the board.

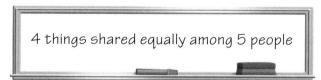

> 4 things shared equally among 5 people

Can you tell me a story about 4 things that are shared equally among 5 people?

Collect a few examples. Be sure students use items that can be cut (muffins, apples, bananas, brownies, granola bars, etc.).

Do you think each person's share is exactly 1, greater than 1, or less than 1?

Students might say:

"Less than 1. There are more people than things, so each person gets less than 1 whole."

Have students write a story and work with a partner to solve it. Tell students to use brownies or pictures to show their solution. When students have finished, discuss their solution strategies.

Students might say:

"I drew 4 rectangles. I divided each rectangle into 5 equal parts and put a different name in each part. I counted the parts for each person. Each person's share is $\frac{4}{5}$."

Show (or have the students show) the solutions on the board.

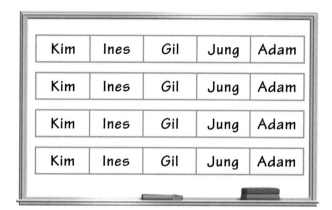

Kim	Ines	Gil	Jung	Adam
Kim	Ines	Gil	Jung	Adam
Kim	Ines	Gil	Jung	Adam
Kim	Ines	Gil	Jung	Adam

ELL English Language Learners

Partner Talk Have pairs discuss their solutions. More proficient speakers can explain what the solution shows using words such as *group* and *share equally* in their descriptions. Less proficient speakers can point to the parts of the solution.

Additional Resource

Student Math Handbook pages 61–62

Differentiation in Investigation 2

Mathematics in This Investigation

The mathematics focuses on seeing and using equivalencies among fractions represented by pattern block pieces.

Additional Resource: *Visualizing Fraction Equivalencies,* pages 113–114 (See Curriculum Unit 7)

Understanding the Mathematics

Students find many ways to make a whole or a given fraction, and they write equations that accurately match their work. They see and use equivalencies among the pattern block shapes, and can break a fraction into 2 (or more) parts (e.g., $\frac{1}{2} = \frac{1}{3} + \frac{1}{6}$) in order to place pieces in more than 1 hexagon. They reason about equivalencies to determine whether a pattern block design is half yellow, and they can generate elaborate designs that are half yellow. Students understand that, in equivalent fractions, each numerator has the same relationship to the denominator (e.g., the denominator is double the numerator in all fractions that equal $\frac{1}{2}$).

Option: Assign the Extension activity.

Partially Understanding the Mathematics

Students figure out the fraction that each pattern block represents by thinking about how many of a certain shape make a whole hexagon (e.g., it takes 2 red trapezoids, so 1 red is $\frac{1}{2}$). They find different ways to make a whole or a given fraction, though they gravitate towards combinations that use the same denominator, particularly when working numerically. Students are beginning to use equivalencies among the pattern block shapes as they play the *Fraction Cookie* game (e.g., if they roll $\frac{1}{2}$, they know they can take 1 trapezoid, 3 triangles, or 1 rhombus and 1 triangle), but other common fraction equivalents may still be less familiar. They can generate pattern block designs that are half yellow, but determining whether someone else's design is half yellow is more challenging.

Option: Assign the Practice activity.

Not Understanding the Mathematics

Students figure out the fraction that each pattern block represents by covering a hexagon with multiple pieces of each block. They may need to do this for most activities. They use pattern blocks to find different ways to make a whole or a given fraction. Students are just beginning to make sense of fraction notation. They typically have just one image for each fraction on the cube in the *Fraction Cookie* game (e.g., if they roll $\frac{1}{2}$, they have a hard time thinking about any option other than 1 red trapezoid). Generating fairly simple half-yellow pattern-block designs, or analyzing someone else's, is challenging.

Option: Assign the Intervention activity.

Investigation 2 Quiz

In addition to your observations and students' work in Investigation 2, the Quiz (R61) can be used to gather more information.

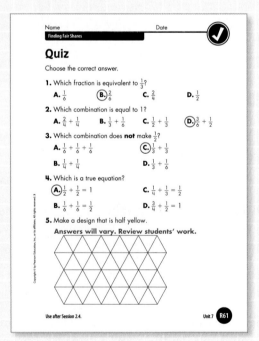

Intervention

30 MIN **INDIVIDUALS**

Is It Half Yellow?

Use anytime after Session 2.4.

Math Focus Points

◆ Using representations to combine fractions that sum to 1 (e.g., $\frac{1}{4} + \frac{3}{4} = 1$, $\frac{1}{3} + \frac{1}{3} + \frac{1}{3} = 1$, $\frac{1}{2} + \frac{1}{4} + \frac{1}{4} = 1$)

Materials: pattern blocks, markers or crayons (red, blue, green, and yellow), M18 , R62

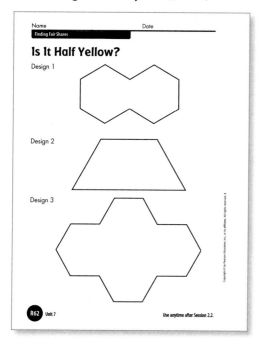

Distribute pattern blocks, markers or crayons, and a copy of Is It Half Yellow? (R62) to each student.

Take one hexagon. Build another hexagon shape using the other pattern block shapes. Have students share the combinations of blocks they used. Let's use this set of shapes to fill the first design on your sheet. Place your yellow hexagon on the left side of the design. Is half of the design yellow?

Have students trace the edge of the pattern block that defines the middle of the design and color the left side yellow. What part of your design is yellow? What part of your design is not colored in?

Students use the other pattern blocks from the set to fill in the rest of the design. They can trace around

each block and color in the shapes.

Now that you have filled the design, what part of the design is yellow? If this were a fancy cracker and you ate the yellow part and your friend ate the other parts, would it be fair? Would you both get the same amount even though you got one big piece and they got several smaller pieces? Why or why not?

Repeat using Design 2. Reinforce with students that they are considering the area of the design as being half yellow rather than the number of blocks used to fill the design.

Before students fill in Design 3, have them take two hexagons and, using the other pattern shapes, build two additional hexagon shapes. For the third design, use this new set of pattern blocks to fill in the design. As you fill in and then color the design, think about whether or not this design is half yellow.

Students share how they filled Design 3. Again focus the discussion on how they can explain whether or not their design is half yellow.

Have students use the set of blocks that they used to fill Design 3 to make a new design. They should build their design on Triangle Paper (M18), trace around each block and then color it. To emphasize the "whole," have them outline their entire design using a black marker. Students can make other half-yellow designs, increasing the number of hexagons used by one for each new design.

ELL **English Language Learners**

Provide a Word List Write the words *hexagon* and *half* on the board. Review the meaning of each with students. Have students copy each word on a sheet of paper. Help them draw pictures to illustrate the words. Allow students to refer to this list as needed.

Additional Resource

Student Math Handbook pages 63–64

Practice

20 MIN | **INDIVIDUALS**

Identifying Equivalent Fractions

Use anytime after Session 2.2.

Math Focus Points

◆ Identifying equivalent fractional parts

Vocabulary: equivalent fractions

Materials: pattern blocks, M16, R63

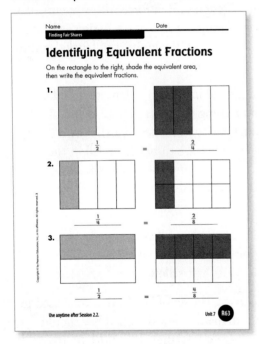

Materials to Prepare: On a copy of Hexagon Cookies (M16), draw a line between the 2nd and 3rd rows. Then draw a line to divide each column so 6 pairs of hexagons are created. Make a copy for each student.

Remind students of the discussion they had in Session 2.2 about equivalent fractions.

When you made trades in the Fraction Cookie game, you were finding equivalent fractions. For example, [Philip] traded 3 greens for a red. How can we show that trade? Which equivalent fractions can we write for it?

Draw the following hexagons on the board and write the equation underneath.

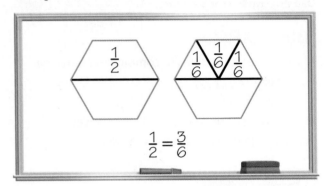

$\frac{1}{2}$ and $\frac{3}{6}$ are equivalent fractions because they name the same amount.

Distribute pattern blocks and the prepared copies of M16. Tell students to copy the example from the board and show 2 more pairs of equivalent fractions, writing an equation for each.

Use the pattern blocks to model the fractions. Think of the trades you made while playing Fraction Cookie to help you find equivalent fractions.

Give students time to work. Then collect examples and draw them (or have volunteers draw them) on the board. Students should model the following pairs of equivalent fractions: $\frac{1}{3} = \frac{2}{6}$ and $\frac{2}{3} = \frac{4}{6}$.

Distribute copies of Identifying Equivalent Fractions (R63).

Additional Resource

Student Math Handbook pages 63–64

Extension

35 MIN   PAIRS

Adding and Subtracting Fraction Cookies

Use anytime after Session 2.4.

Math Focus Points

◆ Using representations to combine fractions that sum to 1 (e.g., $\frac{1}{4} + \frac{3}{4} = 1$, $\frac{1}{3} + \frac{1}{3} + \frac{1}{3} = 1$, $\frac{1}{2} + \frac{1}{4} + \frac{1}{4} = 1$)

Materials: pattern blocks, fraction number cubes (2 in one color and 1 in a different color), M15 (1 per pair), M16 (3 per student)

Tell students that they will play two variations of the *Fraction Cookie* game today. Demonstrate the Intermediate game, *Adding Fraction Cookies*, first.

In this variation, you roll two fraction cubes. You will *add* the amounts and collect that amount of cookies in pattern blocks. Then you continue playing as you played in the original game.

Let's go through one example together. On my first turn, I rolled $\frac{1}{2}$ and $\frac{1}{3}$, which have a sum of $\frac{5}{6}$. I took a red trapezoid and a blue rhombus. Do I have the fewest pieces? How could I trade so that I have fewer pieces?

Distribute the materials. Have pairs play the Intermediate game, recording their work on Hexagon Cookies (M16).

Next, demonstrate how to play the Advanced variation, *Adding and Subtracting Fraction Cookies*.

In this variation, you start with two whole hexagon cookies. You will roll *two cubes of one color* and *a third cube of a different color*. You will *add* the amounts on the first 2 cubes and then *subtract* the amount on the third cube from your collection.

Let's go through another example together. On my first turn, I rolled $\frac{1}{6}$ and $\frac{1}{6}$, which have a sum of $\frac{2}{6}$, or $\frac{1}{3}$. I took a blue rhombus. Then I rolled $\frac{1}{2}$. I traded one of the yellow hexagons for two red trapezoids and then subtracted $\frac{1}{2}$ by putting one red trapezoid back.

Have pairs play the Advanced game using a new copy of M16.

ELL English Language Learners

Rephrase Some English Language Learners may have difficulty understanding complicated directions. Help by rephrasing the new directions. For the Intermediate variation, say: Roll two cubes. Add the fractions. Take the pattern blocks. For the Advanced variation, say: Roll two cubes. Add the fractions. Take the pattern blocks. Roll the third cube. Subtract by putting a block back.

Additional Resource

Student Math Handbook page 64

Differentiation in Investigation 3

Mathematics in This Investigation

The mathematics focuses on developing an understanding of decimals in relation to their fractional equivalents, mainly using the context of money.

Understanding the Mathematics

Students are familiar with decimal notation and notation for money and use it accurately. They know common fraction and decimal equivalents (e.g., $0.5 = \frac{1}{2}$, $.25 = \frac{1}{4}$) and see relationships between different notations (e.g., $2\frac{1}{4}$ and 2.25) and the situations that each represents. They accurately divide or share amounts of money using what they know about equivalencies (e.g., 4 quarters in a dollar).

Option: Assign the **Extension** activity.

Partially Understanding the Mathematics

Students are familiar with notation for money ($, .), but they are just beginning to understand decimal notation (e.g., 0.25) and how it connects to fractional amounts and situations. They know some common fraction equivalents (e.g., $0.5 = \frac{1}{2}$). Students know money equivalents (e.g., $1 = 4 quarters), but they are just beginning to use them to reason and solve problems. Typically, students rely on pictures or play money to divide or share amounts of money.

Option: Assign the **Practice** activity.

Not Understanding the Mathematics

Students may be familiar with notation for money ($, .), but they have little sense of the meaning behind it. They may know some money equivalents (e.g., $1 = 4 quarters), but they are unsure of others. Students' strategies for solving problems about sharing or dividing amounts of money among a group of people rely mainly on modeling the situation with play money.

Option: Assign the **Intervention** activity.

Investigation 3 Quiz

In addition to your observations and students' work in Investigation 3, the Quiz (R64) can be used to gather more information.

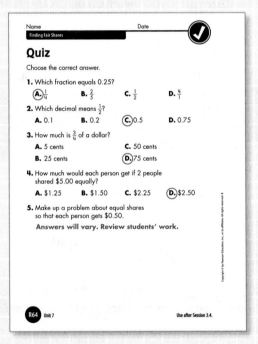

Intervention

30 MIN   PAIRS

Making and Sharing $1

Use anytime after Session 3.2.

Math Focus Points

◆ Identifying equivalent fractions and decimals for values involving halves and fourths (e.g., $\frac{1}{2} = 0.50$, $\frac{1}{4} = 0.25$, $2\frac{1}{2} = 2.5$)

◆ Reading, writing, and interpreting the meaning of the decimal numbers 0.50, 0.25, and numbers greater than 1 with these decimal portions, such as 2.5 and 2.25

Materials: pennies (100 per pair), coin sets (1 per pair), paper $1 bill, chart paper

· ·

Briefly review coin equivalencies with students.

Hold up the $1 bill. What do you know about a dollar? How many pennies equal 1 dollar? How many dimes? Nickels? Quarters? Record these equivalencies on chart paper.

Distribute coin sets. Ask students to make 1 dollar using only dimes and nickels. Record some of these combinations on the chart.

Can you make 1 dollar using a mix of quarters, dimes, and nickels? Give students time to assemble 1 dollar with these coins. Have students share their combinations as you record them on the chart.

Some Ways to Make $1.00

100 pennies

20 nickels

10 dimes

4 quarters

3 quarters, 2 dimes, 1 nickel

2 quarters, 5 dimes

1 quarter, 5 nickels, 50 pennies

9 dimes, 1 nickel, 5 pennies

Next have students practice sharing $1 between two people.

Suppose you had 2 quarters and 5 dimes and you wanted to share the $1 equally with your partner. Show me what each person's share would be.

How much does each person get?

Students might say:

"Each person would get 1 quarter and 2 dimes. Then you have to split the extra dime into 10 pennies. Each person gets 5 pennies."

How can you say each person's share using a fraction? *($\frac{1}{2}$ dollar each)* How can you tell each person's share using a decimal? *($0.50 each)* From the chart that includes quarters, dimes, and nickels, select another combination of coins for students to share between 2 people. Reinforce that the fraction and decimal amounts will be the same ($\frac{1}{2}$, 0.50). However, the combination of coins will be different.

Repeat the process for sharing $1 among 4 people. Have students show at least 2 different coin combinations for each. Reinforce the fraction and decimal notation ($\frac{1}{4}$, 0.25).

ELL English Language Learners

Provide a Word List Help students write the name of each U.S. coin and its value on a sheet of paper. You may want to provide coins from a coin set for students to tape onto their papers. Allow students to refer to this list as needed.

Additional Resource

Student Math Handbook pages 37–38, 65

Practice

25 MIN **PAIRS**

Sharing More Dollars

Use anytime after Session 3.1.

Math Focus Points

◆ Identifying equivalent fractions and decimals for values involving halves and fourths (e.g., $\frac{1}{2} = 0.50$, $\frac{1}{4} = 0.25$, $2\frac{1}{2} = 2.5$)

Vocabulary: decimal, decimal point

Materials: pennies (100 per pair), coin sets (1 per pair), paper $1 bills (10 per pair), R65

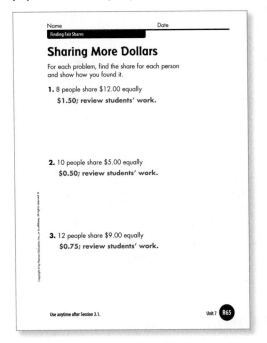

Remind students of the Sharing Dollars problems they solved in Session 3.1. Then review how to write money amounts using decimal numbers.

How do you use a decimal to write 25 cents? How do you use a decimal to write 1 dollar and 50 cents? Where does the decimal point go?

Explain that students will be solving more Sharing Dollars problems. The problems involve sharing larger amounts of money.

Write the following problems on the board.

> 6 people share $9.00 equally
>
> 8 people share $10.00 equally

Have students write each situation and find the share for each person. Students may use play money or draw pictures to solve. When students have finished, collect their solutions and strategies.

How much would each person get if 6 people share $9.00 equally?

Students might say:

"I gave each person a $1 bill. Then I traded in the remaining three $1 bills for 12 quarters. I passed out 2 quarters to each person. So each person got $1.50."

How much would each person get if 8 people share $10.00 equally?

Students might say:

"1 dollar is 4 quarters, so 10 dollars are 40 quarters. I drew 8 equal groups of 5 quarters each. Each person got 5 quarters, or $1.25."

Distribute copies of Sharing More Dollars (R65).

ELL **English Language Learners**

Rephrase Some English Language Learners may be confused if the word *bill* is used instead of *dollar*. The word *bill* has many other meanings—a bird's beak, a hat brim, a statement of money owed, a statute in draft, etc. Be sure to address any confusion.

Additional Resource

Student Math Handbook page 65

Extension

30 MIN **PAIRS**

My Own Sharing Puzzles
Use anytime after Session 3.2.

Math Focus Points

◆ Identifying equivalent fractions and decimals for values involving halves and fourths (e.g., $\frac{1}{2} = 0.50$, $\frac{1}{4} = 0.25$, $2\frac{1}{2} = 2.5$)

Materials: connecting cubes, blank paper (3 sheets per student), R66

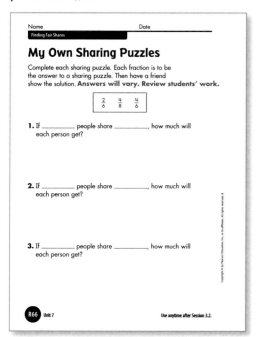

Remind students of the sharing problems they made up in Session 3.2. Today you will make up 3 sharing puzzles for your partner to solve.

Write the following fractions on the board.

$$\frac{2}{3} \qquad \frac{3}{6} \qquad \frac{6}{8}$$

Each fraction will be the answer to a sharing puzzle. For example, which fraction is the answer to this puzzle? Write the problem on the board and read aloud to students.

If 6 people share 4 apples, how much of an apple will each person get?

Students might say:

"Divide 3 whole apples into 6 halves and give each person $\frac{1}{2}$ of an apple. Divide the fourth apple into 6 sixths and give each person $\frac{1}{6}$ of an apple. Because $\frac{1}{2} + \frac{1}{6} = \frac{2}{3}$, each person gets $\frac{2}{3}$ of an apple."

Give students about 20 minutes to write their puzzles, one to a page. Students may use cubes or draw pictures to help them construct each puzzle. Provide scrap paper for students to draw on so as not to give the answer away.

When students have finished, have partners swap puzzles and identify the answer for each.

If time allows, invite volunteers to read one of their own puzzles aloud for other students to solve.

Distribute copies of My Own Sharing Puzzles (R66).

ELL English Language Learners

Partner Talk Review the names of the following fractions: $\frac{1}{6}, \frac{1}{3}, \frac{1}{2}, \frac{3}{6}, \frac{2}{3}, \frac{6}{8}$. Have pairs of ELL students explain how they solved their partner's puzzle to practice English. Beginner ELLs may only be able to respond with short phrases. More proficient speakers can help by adding more information.

Additional Resource

Student Math Handbook page 63

Differentiation in Investigation 1

Mathematics in This Investigation

The mathematics focuses on adding multiples of 10 and 100 to, and subtracting them from, 3-digit numbers.

Understanding the Mathematics

Students fluently add multiples of 10 and 100 to, and subtract them from, 3-digit numbers. They solve such problems mentally, knowing which digits will change and which will not change. They see and use relationships between problems (e.g., $500 - 38$, $550 - 38$, and $550 - 138$), and they can use a representation or context to explain why the answer to one problem is more or less than a related problem.

Option: Assign the Extension activity.

Partially Understanding the Mathematics

Students accurately add multiples of 10 and 100 to, and subtract them from, 3-digit numbers. They may use number lines, 100 grids, or 100 charts to solve such problems. Creating representations or using a context to think through a problem helps these students begin to see relationships among problems. Students use these relationships to help them estimate the number of hundreds there will be, or to determine which digits will change and which will not change, in an answer.

Option: Assign the Practice activity.

Not Understanding the Mathematics

Students are still developing efficient strategies for adding multiples of 10 and 100 to, and subtracting them from, 3-digit numbers. They likely need to model the problems. These students may still be thinking and working mostly with tens and ones. Because each problem tends to be a challenging problem in and of itself, comparing two problems to think about the relationships between them is challenging. Students find it challenging to estimate the number of hundreds there will be, or to determine which digits will change and which will not change, in an answer.

Option: Assign the Intervention activity.

Investigation 1 Quiz

In addition to your observations and students' work in Investigation 1, the Quiz (R67) can be used to gather more information.

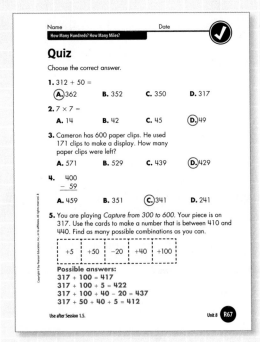

Intervention

25 MIN **INDIVIDUALS**

Subtracting Multiples of 10

Use anytime after Session 1.2.

Math Focus Points

◆ Adding multiples of 10 and 100 to, and subtracting them from, 3-digit numbers

Vocabulary: hundreds, tens, ones

Materials: 301–600 charts (as needed)

Write $472 - 100$ on the board. Ask students to think about the problem. Placing it in a familiar context might help. Suppose that I had 472 paper clips and I took away one box of 100 paper clips. How many paper clips would I have?

Discuss students' strategies, then focus on how subtracting 100 from 472 changed the number. We started with 472 paper clips. We ended with 372 paper clips. What do you notice about those 2 numbers?

Students might say:

"The 7 and the 2 stayed the same."

"The 4 changed into a 3."

Encourage students to discuss why the numbers change (or don't). There are 4 hundreds in 472. We took away 1 hundred. How many hundreds were left? There are also 7 tens and 2 ones in 472. Did we take away any tens? Any ones?

Next pose a related problem. This time, I took away one box of 100 and 20 more paper clips. Now how many are left?

$$\begin{array}{r} 472 \\ -100 \\ \hline 372 \end{array} \qquad \begin{array}{r} 472 \\ -120 \\ \hline \end{array}$$

Encourage students to use the first problem to help them solving the second. How many hundreds will there be in the answer? How do you know? After students solve the problem, discuss their strategies. If no one subtracted 100 and then 20, be sure to highlight that method. We know from the first problem that $472 - 100 = 372$. What do we still have left to subtract? How could we solve $372 - 20$? Acknowledge that, in the second problem, you subtracted more, so your answer was less.

Then, have a similar discussion about what changed (and didn't). We started with 472 and ended with 352. What do you notice about those 2 numbers? Again, discuss why both the hundreds and the tens number changed but the ones number remained the same.

Pose another pair of related problems, one at a time, following the same process described above.

$$\begin{array}{r} 559 \\ -200 \\ \hline \end{array} \qquad \begin{array}{r} 559 \\ -220 \\ \hline \end{array}$$

ELL **English Language Learners**

Provide a Word List Write the words *hundreds, tens,* and *ones* on chart paper. Under each word, list examples of each type of number (e.g., 100, 200, 300; 10, 20, 30; 1, 2, 3). Reinforce the language associated with these numbers with sentences. For example: *Two hundreds* is 200; *3 tens* is 30.

Additional Resource

Student Math Handbook page 36

Practice

20 MIN   PAIRS

Addition and Subtraction Practice

Use anytime after Session 1.2.

Math Focus Points

◆ Adding multiples of 10 and 100 to, and subtracting them from, 3-digit numbers

Materials: R68

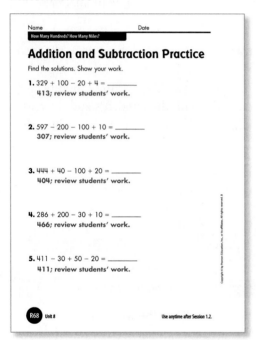

Name _____ Date _____

How Many Hundreds? How Many Miles?

Addition and Subtraction Practice

Find the solutions. Show your work.

1. 329 + 100 − 20 + 4 = _____
413; review students' work.

2. 597 − 200 − 100 + 10 = _____
307; review students' work.

3. 444 + 40 − 100 + 20 = _____
404; review students' work.

4. 286 + 200 − 30 + 10 = _____
466; review students' work.

5. 411 − 30 + 50 − 20 = _____
411; review students' work.

R68 Unit 8   Use anytime after Session 1.2.

· ·

Write the following equations on the board.

$$368 + 40 - 30 - 50 = \underline{\hspace{1cm}}$$
$$494 - 100 + 50 + 100 = \underline{\hspace{1cm}}$$
$$512 + 40 + 30 - 50 = \underline{\hspace{1cm}}$$

These are sample equations from a game of *Capture from 300 to 600*. Work with your partner to find the solution for each.

Give students about 10 minutes to work. Then discuss the ending number, or solution, for each equation.

In the first equation, is the solution greater or less than the starting number? Why is that?

Students might say:

"The answer's less because I took away more than I added on."

How did you solve the second equation?

Students might say:

"I added 50 to 494 because adding 100 cancels out subtracting 100."

In the third equation, which digit stayed the same? Why is that?

Students might say:

"The ones place stayed the same because we only added and subtracted 10s, we didn't add or subtract any ones."

Distribute copies of Addition and Subtraction Practice (R68).

ELL **English Language Learners**

Partner Talk Have ELL pairs describe how they solved each equation. Less proficient speakers may only be able to use short phrases. More proficient speakers can add information to help create a more detailed explanation.

Additional Resource

Student Math Handbook

Game: *Capture from 300 to 600* SMH G1–G2

Materials: 301–600 Charts, Plus/Minus Cards, chips, game pieces, M17

Extension

20 MIN **PAIRS**

Extending a Set of Problems

Use anytime after Session 1.3.

Math Focus Points

◆ Adding multiples of 10 and 100 to, and subtracting them from, 3-digit numbers

Materials: R69

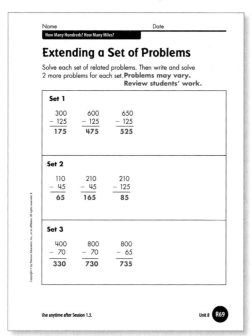

Remind students of the related subtraction problems they solved in Session 1.3. Today you will solve another set of related problems. Then you will extend the set by creating more problems. You may use numbers in the thousands if you like.

Write the following problems on the board.

200	200	600	630
− 20	− 120	− 120	− 120

Work with your partner to solve these problems. Then write 3 more that extend the set.

Have volunteers explain the relationships in their extension problems and how they used them to find the answers.

Students might say:

"I wrote problems that started with 200 more than the problem before it. The difference is 200 more each time."

830	1,030	1,230
− 120	− 120	− 120
710	910	1,110

Students might say:

"I took one away from each number in the fourth problem so that the difference stayed the same. Then I did that 2 more times."

629	628	627
− 119	− 118	− 117
510	510	510

Distribute copies of Extending a Set of Problems (R69).

ELL **English Language Learners**

Rephrase Some English Language Learners may have difficulty with the words *related* and *extend*. Explain the meanings of these words with students using words with which they are more familiar.

Additional Resource

Student Math Handbook pages 32–35

Differentiation in Investigation 2

Mathematics in This Investigation

The mathematics focuses on using different strategies to efficiently add 3-digit numbers.

Additional Resource: *Addition Strategies,* pages 152–154 (See Curriculum Unit 8)

Understanding the Mathematics

Students are fluent with more than one strategy for adding 3-digit numbers or several 2-digit numbers. They use strategies that break the numbers apart in reasonable and efficient ways (e.g., adding by place or adding one number on in parts). They keep track of and recombine the parts accurately, and use clear and concise notation. They use knowledge about combinations of 10, 100, and 1,000 in their work. Students understand why the strategy of making an equivalent problem works. They often choose a strategy based on the numbers in the problem. In making estimates about the number of hundreds in a sum, students use what they know about the tens and the ones.

Option: Assign the **Extension** activity.

Partially Understanding the Mathematics

Students are fluent with one strategy for addition, and they generally use it to add 3-digit numbers or several 2-digit numbers. Their strategy is typically adding by place or adding one number on in parts. They are still developing efficiency and accuracy with a second strategy. They use knowledge about combinations of 10 and 100 in their work. Making an equivalent problem may be a new strategy for these students, but creating a representation helps them make sense of it. When they estimate the number of hundreds in a sum, they pay attention to the tens, but may ignore the ones.

Option: Assign the **Practice** activity.

Not Understanding the Mathematics

Students are not yet fluent with one strategy for addition. They likely have a strategy that they typically use (e.g., adding by place), but they are still developing efficiency and accuracy with it. They may still need to directly model the problem with stickers. They may have trouble keeping track of the parts and recombining them accurately. Students may be familiar with combinations of 10 and 100, but they may not always see how these combinations could be useful in their work. When they estimate the number of hundreds in a sum, they pay attention only to the number of hundreds in each number.

Option: Assign the **Intervention** activity.

Investigation 2 Quiz

In addition to your observations and students' work in Investigation 2, the Quiz (R70) can be used to gather more information.

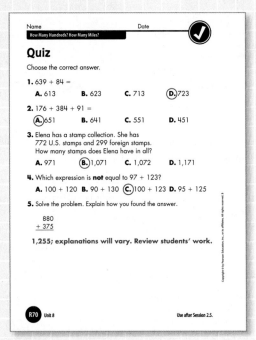

Intervention

25 MIN   INDIVIDUALS

Adding Smaller 3-Digit Numbers

Use anytime after Session 2.2.

Math Focus Points

◆ Solving addition problems with 3-digit numbers

◆ Identifying addition strategies by focusing on how each strategy starts

Vocabulary: estimate

Materials: M9 (optional)

Write 218 + 134 = _____ on the board and ask students to estimate about how much the sum would be. How many hundreds will the answer have? How do you know how many hundreds?

Students might say:

"Look at the numbers in the hundreds place. There are 2 hundreds in 218 and 1 hundred in 134. So, there are 3 hundreds in the answer."

"I agree. The 18 and the 34 don't make another 100, so I know the answer will have just 3 hundreds."

If students struggle with finding the number of hundreds, ask them to represent the numbers with 100 Grids (M9). Show me how to use the 100 grids to figure out how many hundreds the sum will have.

Summarize students' thinking, recording 200 + 100 = 300 on the board. So one way to begin solving this problem is to combine the hundreds. We could say our *first step* was to add 200 + 100 to get 300.

$$218 + 134 = \underline{}$$
$$200 + 100 = \underline{300}$$

If we wanted to finish solving this problem, what would our next step be? What do we have left to do?

Refer students to their 100 grids to help them see that they still have the tens and the ones left to add. Let's add the tens next. What equation should I write? Continue working through the problem, and recording the steps on the board. Once the tens and ones have been added, discuss how to combine these parts to get the answer.

$$218 + 134 = \underline{352}$$
$$200 + 100 = 300$$
$$10 + 30 = 40$$
$$8 + 4 = 12$$
$$300 + 40 + 12 = 352$$

If time remains, follow the same steps with another problem: 327 + 142.

ELL   English Language Learners

Provide a Word List Write the words *estimate* and *sum* on chart paper. Review the meaning of each word with students. Be aware that some English Language Learners may confuse the word *sum* with *some*.

Additional Resource

Student Math Handbook pages 20–24

Practice

20 MIN   GROUPS

Adding 3-Digit Numbers
Use anytime after Session 2.4.

Math Focus Points
◆ Solving addition problems with 3-digit numbers

Vocabulary: estimate

Materials: R71

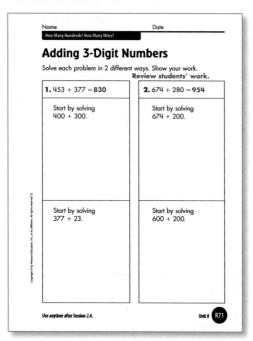

Name _____ Date _____

How Many Hundreds? How Many Miles?

Adding 3-Digit Numbers

Solve each problem in 2 different ways. Show your work.
Review students' work.

1. 453 + 377 = **830**

Start by solving
400 + 300.

Start by solving
377 + 23.

2. 674 + 280 = **954**

Start by solving
674 + 200.

Start by solving
600 + 200.

Use anytime after Session 2.4.   Unit 8 R71

· ·

Students use 2 different starter problems to solve a problem. Write the problem and the 2 starter problems on the board.

$$537 + 389 = \underline{\quad}$$

$$500 + 300 = \underline{\quad} \quad 500 + 389 = \underline{\quad}$$

First ask students to make an estimate, perhaps by thinking about how many hundreds there will be in the answer.

Students might say:

"There are 5 hundreds in 537 and 3 hundreds in 389. There's 1 more hundred because 37 + 89 is more than 100. So the answer will have 9 hundreds."

Pairs solve the problem in 2 ways, using each of the first steps on the board. Give students time to work. Then discuss the next steps for each strategy.

Let's talk about the strategy where the first step is 500 + 300. What did you do next? Most students add the tens (30 + 80 = 110), add the ones (7 + 9 = 16), and then add each of the sums (800 + 110 + 16 = 926).

The first step of the second starter problem is 500 + 389. What did you do next? In this first step, one number is kept whole and the other is added on in parts. Some students add the 30 and then the 7, while others add 11 and then 26.

Compare the actual answer to the students' estimates. Did we make a reasonable estimate? Does the answer have 9 hundreds?

Distribute copies of Adding 3-Digit Numbers (R71).

ELL English Language Learners

Model Thinking Aloud Model the language used to describe each starter problem. Break the numbers apart into hundreds, tens, and ones; keep one number whole and add the other in parts.

Additional Resource

Student Math Handbook pages 20–24

Extension

20 MIN   PAIRS

Making Equivalent Problems

Use anytime after Session 2.4.

Math Focus Points

◆ Solving addition problems with 3-digit numbers

Materials: R72

Name _____ **Date** _____

How Many Hundreds? How Many Miles?

Making Equivalent Problems

Solve the problems. Try to make an equivalent
problem for at least one problem in each set.

Set 1

$268 + 374 =$ __642__ $397 + 454 =$ __851__

Sample answer:
$400 + 451 = 851$

Set 2

$149 + 252 =$ __401__ $643 + 174 =$ __817__

Sample answer:
$150 + 251 = 401$

Set 3

$289 + 411 =$ __700__ $373 + 166 =$ __539__

Sample answer:
$300 + 400 = 700$

R72 Unit 8   Use anytime after Session 2.4.

Remind students that in Session 2.1 they changed
the numbers in a problem to create an equivalent
problem that was easier to solve. You can look at a
problem and decide whether this would be a good
strategy to use to solve it.

Write the following problems on the board.

$$492 + 238 = \underline{\qquad}$$
$$354 + 442 = \underline{\qquad}$$

Which of these problems would be easier to
solve if you made an equivalent problem?

Students might say:

"I think it'd work better for the first
problem. I would turn 492 into 500
and add on 230."

How did [Zhang] get from 492 to 500? *(He added
8.)* Where did the 8 come from? *(From the 238.)* If
you take 8 from the 238 to add to the 492, what
must you do to 238? *(Subtract 8.)* What is the new
expression? *(500 + 230 = 730)* Note that some
students will see other ways to make an equivalent
problem to efficiently solve the problems.

Give students another set of equations to consider.

$$547 + 271 = \underline{\qquad}$$
$$675 + 226 = \underline{\qquad}$$

Talk with your partner. Decide which problem
would be easier to solve by making an equivalent
problem.

Explain to students that they can choose either
problem to solve. If partners disagree on which
problem is "easier," have each student explain why
he or she chose the problem to solve. Most students
will choose the second problem and suggest
$700 + 201 = 901$.

Distribute copies of Making Equivalent Problems
(R72).

ELL English Language Learners

Provide Sentence Stems Give students sentence
stems to help them use this strategy. For example:
To find an equivalent expression, first _____
(add an amount to one addend). Then _____
(subtract the same amount from the other addend).

Additional Resource

Student Math Handbook page 24

Differentiation in Investigation 3

Mathematics in This Investigation

The mathematics focuses on solving 3-digit subtraction problems in a variety of contexts.

Understanding the Mathematics

Students interpret a variety of subtraction situations, determine an appropriate solution strategy, and carry it out efficiently and accurately. They keep track of their steps and solutions and use mathematical notation to clearly show their thinking.

Option: Assign the Extension activity.

Partially Understanding the Mathematics

Students interpret a variety of subtraction situations, determine an appropriate solution strategy, and carry it out accurately. They may still be developing efficient strategies, occasionally adding or subtracting smaller groups of tens or hundreds rather than using larger chunks (e.g., subtracting 20 twice instead of subtracting 40). Students keep track of their steps and solutions, and they use mathematical notation to clearly show their thinking, but they may still be developing the ability to do so more efficiently.

Option: Assign the Practice activity.

Not Understanding the Mathematics

Students may interpret some subtraction situations (e.g., removal) more easily than others (e.g., missing part or comparison), and their solution strategies may depend in part on the context of the problem. They may model the problem (e.g., play money) or use a representation (e.g., the number line) to solve the problem, as opposed to using such tools to show their work. They do not use efficient chunks of tens or hundreds (e.g., subtracting 20 twice instead of subtracting 40). Because students' solutions have many steps, it may be a challenge to keep track of their work and use mathematical notation to show their thinking.

Option: Assign the Intervention activity.

Investigation 3 Quiz

In addition to your observations and students' work in Investigation 3, the Quiz (R73) can be used to gather more information.

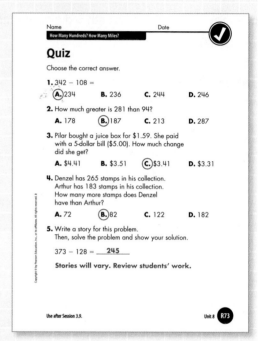

Intervention

25 MIN INDIVIDUALS

Oregon Trail Problems

Use anytime after Session 3.2.

Math Focus Points

◆ Solving subtraction problems that involve comparison, removal, or finding a missing part

Materials: *Student Activity Book* pp. 41–42

In Session 3.2, students solved problems about finding distances between places along the Oregon Trail. Work with students who had difficulty extracting the appropriate numbers needed to solve Problems 1 and 2 on page 41 of the *Student Activity Book*. Ask:

◆ Where did the family start their trip?

◆ What town did they reach after 2 weeks?

◆ How far is it from Council Bluffs to Fort Kearny?

◆ What town did they reach after 1 month?

Draw the following on the board as you talk through the above questions. Ask students to verbalize what the problem is by asking them to find the distance from Fort Kearney to Ash Hollow, or the difference between 504 and 319.

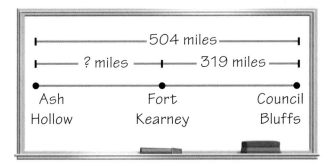

How could we figure out how far it is from Fort Kearny to Ash Hollow?

Students might say:

"We could figure out how much you have to add to the 319 to get 504."

"We could find 504 − 319."

Record equations for both ways of thinking about the problem on the board.

$$319 + \underline{} = 504$$
$$504 - 319 = \underline{}$$

Then students solve the problem. Support students as needed, referring to the model of the problem you've drawn on the board.

Use the same process to work through Problem 2, in which students need to determine the distance between Ash Hollow and Scott's Bluff.

ELL **English Language Learners**

Model Thinking Aloud Model how to find each distance. Find the difference between the distance traveled so far and the distance traveled from the last stop.

Additional Resource

Student Math Handbook pages 32–35

20 MIN | PAIRS

Practice

Lunch Orders

Use anytime after Session 3.7.

Math Focus Points

◆ Solving addition problems with more than 2 addends

Materials: chart paper, R74

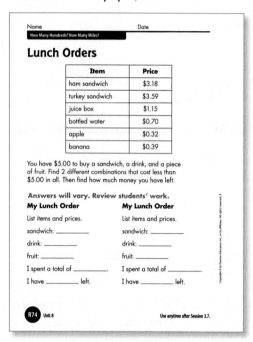

Imagine that you have $10 to buy 3 lunch items for yourself and 2 friends. What can each person have for lunch? List the lunch items and prices, and tell how much you spent and how much is left.

Give students time to work. Encourage them to use equations to show their solutions. Then discuss a few solutions. Who made a lunch order that added up to an amount that was very close to $10?

cheese sandwich	$3.27
hamburger	$4.88
bowl of soup	$1.48

Engage all students to think about the lunch order. Does [Kelley's] order work?

Ask the students to explain how they chose their lunch items and how they figured out the total price and the amount of change they'd get from a $10 bill. How do you know it doesn't go over $10?

Students might say:

"If you add $5 + $3.50 + $1.50, that equals $10. But each thing cost less than that so she spent less that $10."

If time allows, have students use $10 to buy 4 lunch items for themselves and 3 friends. Then distribute copies of Lunch Orders (R74).

Write the following information on the board.

Lunch Menu	
cheese sandwich	$3.27
hamburger	$4.88
hot dog	$2.59
slice of pizza	$2.17
salad	$3.25
bowl of soup	$1.48
free juice box with each purchase	

ELL English Language Learners

Partner Talk Have ELL pairs explain how they chose the lunch items. Beginning English Language Learners may only be able to respond using short phrases. More proficient speakers should be encouraged to use the words *estimate, add, sum,* and *total.*

Additional Resource

Student Math Handbook page 25

Extension

25 MIN **PAIRS**

Subtracting with Larger Numbers

Use anytime after Session 3.6.

Math Focus Points

◆ Solving subtraction problems that involve comparison, removal, or finding a missing part

Materials: chart paper, R75

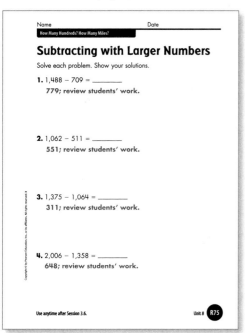

Write the following problem on chart paper.

> On Saturday, 1,256 people attended a baseball game. On Sunday, 982 people attended another baseball game. How many more people attended the game on Saturday than on Sunday?

Give students time to solve the problem. Then have students share strategies. Record one or two strategies on the board.

Students might say:

"I added up: 982 + 18 = 1,000 and 1,000 + 256 = 1,256. I added on 18 and 256, so my answer's 274."

$$982 + \underline{18} = 1,000$$
$$1,000 + \underline{256} = 1,256$$
$$18 + 256 = 274$$

Students might say:

"I thought 982 was pretty close to 1,000. It's only 18 away. So I did 1,256 − 1,000 = 256. But I took away 18 too many so I have to add those back in: 256 + 18 = 274."

You might also discuss how their strategies are the same or different when one of the numbers is over 1,000.

If time remains, have students solve 1,586 − 831. When they have finished, discuss how students kept track of their steps and if they could have been more efficient.

Distribute copies of Subtracting with Larger Numbers (R75).

ELL **English Language Learners**

Provide a Word List On chart paper, write a list of words that are often used in subtraction situations (e.g., *subtract back, subtract in parts, add up in parts,* and *break apart*). Help students use each word in a sentence.

Additional Resource

Student Math Handbook pages 32–35

Differentiation in Investigation 1

Mathematics in This Investigation

The mathematics focuses on distinguishing between polyhedra and nonpolyhedra and on describing properties of 3-dimensional shapes such as edges, vertices, and faces.

Understanding the Mathematics

Students sort 3-D solids according to attributes such as the number and shape of faces. They accurately identify, count, and keep track of faces, edges, and vertices. They immediately know which shapes can be built with straws and build polyhedra according to particular characteristics, often from mental images of 3-D shapes. Students are flexible in their thinking, visualizing and building more than one polyhedron for a given set of specifications.

Option: Assign the **Extension** activity.

Partially Understanding the Mathematics

Students sort 3-D solids. At first, they sort according to attributes such as functionality (e.g., shapes that roll). Shapes that students can imagine transforming into others (e.g., octagonal prisms into cylinders) may seem more like nonpolyhedra than polyhedra. It may not be immediately clear which shapes can or cannot be made with building kits. These students often build polyhedra using a picture or wooden solid as a model. They may build the parts specified and then work to assemble the parts into a 3-D shape. Students may occasionally skip or double-count some components of 3-D shapes (e.g., faces, edges, vertices) as they develop methods for keeping track. They may be surprised that the same set of specifications can result in different-looking shapes.

Option: Assign the **Practice** activity.

Not Understanding the Mathematics

Students sort 3-D solids. Initially, they sort by focusing on the overall shape (e.g., tall). They may end up with many categories, some of which contain only one solid. They are still developing an understanding of the differences between polyhedra and nonpolyhedra. Using an actual solid as a model, students try to build each shape to figure out which can or cannot be made with straws. Building polyhedra with particular specifications is quite difficult, as is counting and keeping track of the components of a particular 3-D shape (e.g., faces, edges, vertices).

Option: Assign the **Intervention** activity.

Investigation 1 Quiz

In addition to your observations and students' work in Investigation 1, the Quiz (R76) can be used to gather more information.

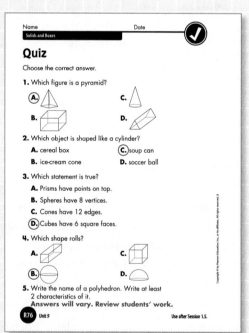

Intervention

20 MIN   **INDIVIDUALS**

Groups of Solids

Use anytime after Session 1.1.

Math Focus Points

◆ Describing the components and properties of different classes of solids, such as polyhedra (3-D shapes having only flat surfaces, such as prisms and pyramids) and nonpolyhedra (such as cones and cylinders)

Materials: geometric solids (1 set per student), construction paper

. . . .

Give each student a sheet of construction paper and ask him or her to draw two large circles on it. Put one set of solids on the table. Hold up the cube. How can you describe this shape?

Students might say:

 "All of its sides are flat."

Put this shape in the circle on the left. Now, find all the other shapes that have *all flat sides*. Put them in the same circle with this shape.

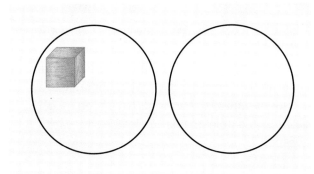

What can you say about the shapes that are left on the table but are *not* in the left circle?

Students might say:

 "All of the sides are not flat. Some are curved."

Put the shapes that do *not* have all flat sides in the other circle. Discuss any solids that students have difficulty deciding where to place. So you sorted the solids into two groups—shapes with all flat sides and shapes that don't have all flat sides. Remove the solids from the paper. Again, hold up the cube.

How *else* can you describe this shape?

Students might say:

 "It does not roll."

Put this shape in the circle on the left. What can you say about this shape that stops it from rolling? What other shapes do *not* roll? Put all the shapes that do not roll in the circle on the left.

Put all the shapes that *do* roll in the other circle. What can you say about these shapes that make them roll? What can you name each group?

ELL English Language Learners

Provide a Word List Have students match each wooden shape to its picture on *Student Math Handbook* page 125 and read the name aloud.

Additional Resource

Student Math Handbook pages 128–129

Practice

25 MIN **PAIRS**

Two Alike, One Different
Use anytime after Session 1.2.

Math Focus Points

◆ Describing the components and properties of different classes of solids such as polyhedra (3-D shapes having only flat surfaces, such as prisms and pyramids) and nonpolyhedra (3-D shapes such as cones and cylinders)

Materials: geometric solids (1 set per pair), chart paper, R77

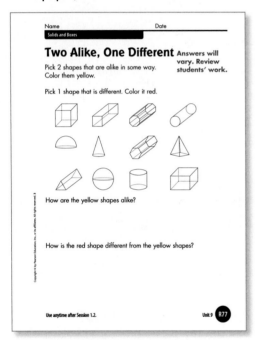

Give each pair a set of solids. One partner will pick three shapes while the other partner closes his or her eyes. You want to pick two shapes that are alike in some way and one shape that is not like them in that way.

Model one round. Ask students to close their eyes. Choose three solids. OK, I'm ready. Open your eyes. You need to identify the two that are alike, tell how they are alike, and tell how the third is different. Which two are alike? Which one is different?

Now students play in pairs, taking turns choosing solids and guessing the rule. As students play, circulate to be sure their sorting schemes make sense. If students have a hard time guessing, encourage the first student to provide a hint by adding another shape that is alike to the group.

After students have played a few rounds, gather the group and ask students to share their rules. Record them on chart paper.

Sorting Schemes

Points at the Top/No Points at the Top

All Flat Faces/Not All Flat Faces

Roll/Does Not Roll

8 Vertices/Not 8 Vertices

6 Faces/Not 6 Faces

Some Curved Sides/No Curved Sides

Some Square Faces/No Square Faces

Distribute copies of Two Alike, One Different (R77).

ELL **English Language Learners**

Provide a Word List Write the words *roll, face, vertex, sides, edges, prisms,* and *pyramids* on chart paper. Then pick a shape and use one of the words in a question. For example: Does this shape *roll*? Continue to ask questions until all of the words have been used. Use gestures and point to relevant features for each question.

Additional Resource

Student Math Handbook
Game: *What's My Shape?* SMH G21
Materials: geometric solids

Extension

25 MIN   **INDIVIDUALS**

Investigating Pyramids

Use anytime after Session 1.5.

Math Focus Points

◆ Visualizing and building polyhedra by using knowledge of their components (faces, edges, and vertices) and how they come together to form the whole

Materials: building kits (from Session 1.3), T102 or *Student Activity Book* p. 13, *Student Math Handbook* p. 128, R78

Name _____ Date _____

Solids and Boxes

Investigating Pyramids

The number of edges on a pyramid is equal to twice the number of sides of the bottom face.

Complete the table below. Figure out the name for each pyramid. (Hint: The names of some prisms might help you.)

Shape of Bottom Face of Pyramid	Number of Sides on Bottom Face	Number of Edges on Pyramid	Name of Pyramid
1. triangle	3	6	triangular pyramid
2. square	4	8	square pyramid
3. pentagon	5	10	pentagonal pyramid
4. hexagon	6	12	hexagonal pyramid
5. octagon	8	16	octagonal pyramid

R78   Unit 9   Use anytime after Session 1.5.

Direct students' attention to Problem 6 on Building Polyhedra (T102) or page 13 of the *Student Activity Book*. I have seen students build a variety of rectangular prisms, including cubes, for this problem. Today you will be building pyramids to see if a pyramid can have exactly 12 edges.

Review pyramids with students using page 128 of the *Student Math Handbook*. Remember that a pyramid comes to a point at the top. A pyramid can have a triangle, square, or any other shape as the bottom face. The shape of the bottom face is what names the type of pyramid. What else do you notice about pyramids? If no one mentions it, point

out that all of the other faces of a pyramid are triangles.

Give students time to build pyramids. Then, look at examples of the pyramids students build, beginning with a triangular pyramid and a square pyramid. Did anyone make a triangular pyramid? How many edges does it have? What about a square pyramid? What do you notice?

Students might say:

"A square has 4 sides, and a square pyramid has 8 edges. I notice that there are 2 times as many edges as there are sides on the square."

So, do you think there is a pyramid that has exactly 12 edges? What can you say about the bottom face of that pyramid?

Students might say:

"If the bottom face had 6 sides, then the pyramid would have 12 edges."

What is a shape with 6 sides called? What is the name of a pyramid with that shape as the bottom face? Challenge students to build a hexagonal pyramid. Does it have 12 edges?

Distribute copies of Investigating Pyramids (R78).

ELL **English Language Learners**

Provide a Word List Write the following list of polygons on the board: *triangle, square, pentagon, hexagon, octagon.* Have students write these words on a sheet of paper and then help them draw a picture for each. Allow them to refer to this illustrated list as needed.

Additional Resource

Student Math Handbook pages 129–130

Differentiation in Investigation 2

Mathematics in This Investigation

The mathematics focuses on seeing and using the relationship between 3-D shapes and 2-D patterns.

Understanding the Mathematics

Students make patterns that hold a certain number of cubes, visualizing how a pattern folds up to cover the faces of a given cube structure, fairly easily. They see, use, and explain patterns (e.g., a pattern for a 2-cube structure can have 8 or 9 squares, depending on whether the top has 1 or 2 cubes). They can visualize why different-looking patterns are congruent, mentally rotating and flipping them. Students are flexible, designing more than one pattern for the same cube structure, and they are comfortable making patterns for triangular pyramids and other 3-D solids.

Option: Assign the **Extension** activity.

Partially Understanding the Mathematics

To make patterns that hold a certain number of cubes, students may trace around the cubes, or they may need to cut out and fold graph paper. They are comfortable with the idea that a 1-cube pattern must have 5 squares, although they may need to test various examples to convince themselves that they do or do not work. For a 2-cube structure, they may be able to see only one 8-square or 9-square pattern, depending on the orientation of the cubes. Students need to physically compare patterns to determine whether they are congruent. Designing more than one pattern for a particular solid, and even just one pattern for a pyramid, may be challenging.

Option: Assign the **Practice** activity.

Not Understanding the Mathematics

Making a pattern that holds a certain number of cubes is challenging, often taking several attempts. Students often begin anew, rather than thinking about how to alter their first attempt. They likely need to cut out patterns to test whether they work or to determine if two patterns are congruent. Designing more than one pattern for a particular solid, and even just one pattern for a pyramid, is likely very challenging.

Option: Assign the **Intervention** activity.

Investigation 2 Quiz

In addition to your observations and students' work in Investigation 2, the Quiz (R79) can be used to gather more information.

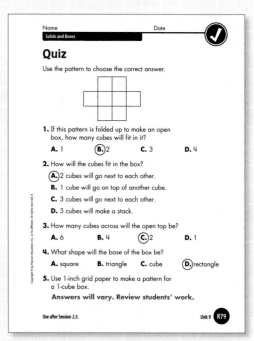

Intervention

20 MIN   INDIVIDUALS

Making Boxes for a Larger Cube

Use anytime after Session 2.1.

Math Focus Points

◆ Determining the number and shapes of the faces of cubes and other rectangular prisms and how they come together to form the whole

◆ Designing patterns that make open boxes for a cube

Materials: cubes from geometric solids set (1 per student), construction paper, scissors, tape

Show students the cube from the geometric solids set. Today you will make a box for this cube. What do you remember about making the open box for the small cube?

Students might say:

"I made it by tracing the faces. Then I cut out the pattern to see if it would fold into a box."

"We figured out that a pattern for a 1-cube box has 5 squares."

Distribute a large cube and one piece of construction paper to each student and tell them to make an open box to hold this large cube. Demonstrate how to trace around each face of the cube. Some students may want to work in pairs so that one student can hold down the cube while the other traces around it. Assist students who might have limitations in manual dexterity. Students should cut out their pattern and test that it does create a box for the cube by folding the sides.

After students have completed their boxes, ask them to compare their patterns with the ones generated by the class in Session 2.1.

Students might say:

"My pattern is bigger because my cube was bigger, but the squares are in the same places."

"The squares in my pattern are larger, but they both use 5 squares and they make the same pattern."

Draw one or two pairs of patterns on chart paper to illustrate students' ideas.

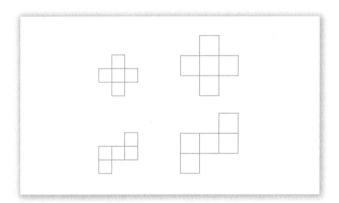

ELL English Language Learners

Rephrase Help English Language Learners by rephrasing parts of the activity using simpler terms. For example: Use the big cube. Make a box for it. Think of the box you made for the small cube.

Additional Resource

Student Math Handbook page 131

Practice

30 MIN   GROUPS

Patterns for Cube Boxes

Use anytime after Session 2.3.

Math Focus Points

◆ Determining the number and shapes of the faces of cubes and other rectangular prisms and how they come together to form the whole

Materials: student-made patterns (1-cube boxes from Session 2.1, 2-cube boxes from Session 2.2), construction paper (2 sheets per group), glue, M16 (as needed), R80

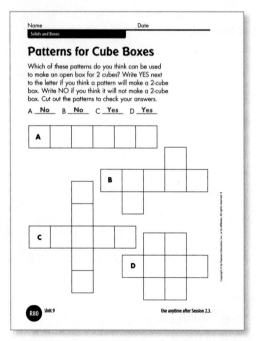

Students will need their patterns for 1-cube boxes and 2-cube boxes.

Sort your patterns into 2 groups—one for the 1-cube boxes and another for the 2-cube boxes. Look carefully at the patterns in each group. Choose one of each type and glue them onto a piece of construction paper. You should make a poster for the 1-cube boxes and another poster for the 2-cube boxes.

Remind students to check that patterns aren't duplicates of each other. Patterns are the same if they are congruent—one can be turned or flipped to fit

directly over the other. You can also challenge them to think about whether their poster shows all of the possible patterns. If they think there is a pattern that would work that is missing, they can make it from Inch Grid Paper (M16).

Give students time to work. Then discuss their posters. What do you notice when you look at the poster for 1-cube boxes? The patterns for 2-cube boxes?

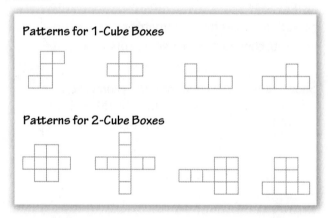

Students might say:

"The 1-cube patterns all have 5 squares."

"The 2-cube patterns have 8 or 9 squares. It depends on whether the cubes were standing up or laying flat."

Distribute copies of Patterns for Cube Boxes (R80).

ELL ◗ **English Language Learners**

Partner Talk Have ELL pairs describe patterns to give them practice with English. More proficient speakers should use words like *square, pattern,* and *cube* while less proficient speakers point to the parts of the pattern.

Additional Resource

Student Math Handbook page 131

Extension

25 MIN   PAIRS

Patterns for 3-Cube Boxes

Use anytime after Session 2.2.

Math Focus Points

◆ Determining the number and shapes of the faces of cubes and other rectangular prisms and how they come together to form the whole

Materials: 1-inch cubes (3 per pair), scissors, construction paper (1 sheet per pair), "Open-Box Pattern Rules" poster (from Session 2.1), M16 (8 per pair), R81

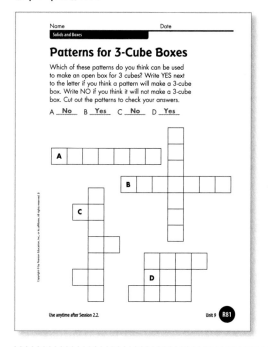

Distribute three 1-inch cubes and 8 copies of Inch Grid Paper (M16) to each pair of students.

We have discussed the patterns you made to build boxes for 1 cube and the patterns you made to build boxes for 2 cubes. Now you'll work with your partner to make open boxes for 3 cubes, following the same rules for the 1-cube and 2-cube boxes.

Direct students' attention to the "Open Box Pattern Rules" poster and briefly review each rule. Explain that the cubes also have to be linked to form one row.

Give students time to work. Then have students show their patterns and explain why they work. What did you need to think about as you designed open boxes to hold 3 cubes?

As students share their strategies, have them post their patterns so that everyone can see them. For each pattern posted, ask students if they agree that it works. If there is disagreement, students should justify their patterns.

What do you notice about the patterns that work? Students should notice that all of the patterns that work contain either 11 or 13 squares, depending on the number of cubes that form the base.

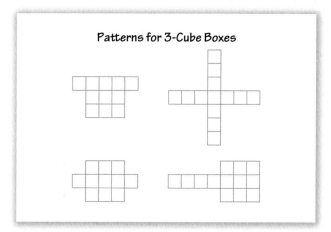

Patterns for 3-Cube Boxes

Distribute copies of Patterns for 3-Cube Boxes (R81).

ELL **English Language Learners**

Provide a Word List Write the words *cube, pattern,* and *square* on chart paper. Review the meaning of each with students. Then have them work together to draw a picture next to each word. Post the list in the classroom for reference.

Additional Resource

Student Math Handbook page 131–133

Differentiation in Investigation 3

Mathematics in This Investigation

The mathematics focuses on structuring rectangular prisms and determining their volume.

Additional Resource: *Strategies for Finding the Number of Cubes in a Box,* page 96 (See Curriculum Unit 9)

Understanding the Mathematics

Students think about the layers of cubes that make up a rectangular prism, and they use their knowledge about factors and multiples to make a variety of prisms with a specific number of cubes. They work from mental images to design patterns to hold such prisms and can make different patterns for the same prism. They use such mental images, as well as their knowledge of multiplication and division, to complete patterns where the sides of the box have not yet been drawn.

Option: Assign the **Extension** activity.

Partially Understanding the Mathematics

Students are coming to understand rectangular prisms as 3-D solids that are made up of layers of cubes. As they make the cube buildings and cut out and test different patterns, they begin to see how knowledge about the factors could help them generate other prisms. Building a pattern from the bottom up is likely challenging for these students, and they need to use cubes and graph paper as they work.

Option: Assign the **Practice** activity.

Not Understanding the Mathematics

Students are still developing an understanding of how the squares on a 2-D piece of graph paper connect to a 3-D solid. When estimating the number of cubes a pattern will hold, they are likely to focus on the number of squares in the pattern rather than what the space inside the box will look like when it is folded. They struggle to visualize 2-D and 3-D shapes and the relationships between them, and they must build cube structures and test patterns as they work. Because students are not yet seeing rectangular prisms as layers of cubes, they may not see how knowledge about multiplication and division, as well as factors and multiples, might help them in their work.

Option: Assign the **Intervention** activity.

Investigation 3 Quiz

In addition to your observations and students' work in Investigation 3, the Quiz (R82) can be used to gather more information.

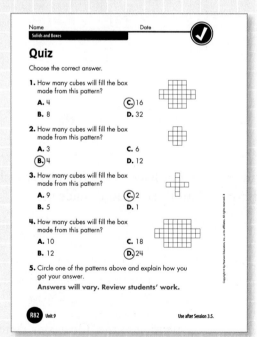

Intervention

25 MIN   INDIVIDUALS

Thinking About Box Patterns

Use anytime after Session 3.1.

Math Focus Points

◆ Communicating about spatial relationships

◆ Determining the number of cubes that will fit in the box made by a given pattern

Materials: connecting cubes, scissors, M23–M24

Give each student a copy of How Many Cubes? (M23) and a pair of scissors. This page shows a pattern for an open box that holds many cubes.

When you worked with this pattern the other day, some people predicted or thought that the box would hold 36 cubes. Now let's see if the box would hold that many cubes. Cut out the pattern and fold it into a box.

Use the following process to help students think about what the squares on the pattern represent and what the space inside the box is like when it is folded. Point to the squares that form the bottom of the box.

◆ How many cubes do you think will fit in the bottom? Put your cubes in to check. Make sure that you connect them so that they will fit.

Now point to the squares on the side of the pattern.

◆ What do you think these squares tell you? Can you fit another row, or another layer of cubes? How many do you think will be in that layer? Let's check.

◆ How many more cubes do you need to fill the box? How did you figure that out? Fill the box with cubes.

◆ How many cubes are in the whole box? How can you figure that out?

Ask students to compare the total number of cubes with the prediction of 36 cubes. So why do you think some people predicted that the box would hold 36 cubes when you just figured out that it holds only 18 cubes?

Students might say:

"I think they counted the squares in the pattern. But that was too many."

Give each student a copy of How Many Cubes? (M24). Students predict how many cubes will fit in the box made from this pattern. Remind them to think about their work with Pattern B as they estimate the number of cubes.

Then follow the same process to determine the number of cubes that will fit in the box made by this pattern. Remind students to first look at the bottom layer of the box and then think about how many layers they will have *before* they make their predictions.

After students are finished with this second box, discuss their strategies. Is the number you thought would fit close to the actual number that does fit? How did you make your prediction for this box?

ELL **English Language Learners**

Rephrase Some English Language Learners might be confused by the word *prediction*. Write the word on the board. Say the word and then have students repeat the word. Explain that a *prediction* is a *guess*.

Additional Resource

Student Math Handbook pages 132–133

Practice

35 MIN   PAIRS

More Box Patterns

Use anytime after Session 3.4.

Math Focus Points

◆ Seeing that the cubes filling a rectangular prism can be decomposed into congruent layers

Materials: M14 (from Unit 5), R83

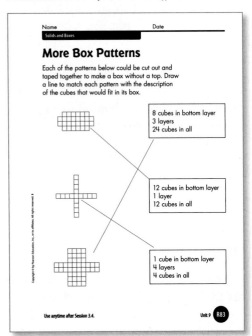

Materials to Prepare: Draw the two patterns shown below on Half-Inch Grid Paper (M14). Make copies and distribute one copy to each pair.

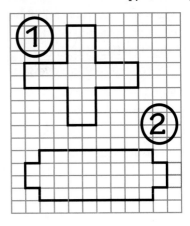

Each of these patterns can be cut out and taped together to make a box without a top. Work with your partner to figure out how many cubes will fit in the box formed by each pattern without cutting out the pattern.

How did you figure out how many cubes would fit?

Students might say:

"We could see that there were 4 cubes in the bottom layer. The flaps show you that there will be 3 layers."

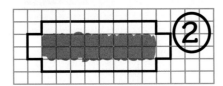

"We colored in the bottom layer. Then we could see that, when you folded up the sides, there would only be one layer."

Distribute copies of More Box Patterns (R83).

ELL ⟩ **English Language Learners**

Suggest a Sequence After students have worked on the problems together, generate and record a clear sequence of steps for finding the number of cubes for a box with more than 1 layer.

1. Find the number of cubes in the bottom layer.

2. Find the number of layers.

3. Add the number of cubes in each layer.

Additional Resource

Student Math Handbook pages 132–133

Extension

30 MIN   PAIRS

Boxes That Hold 16 Cubes

Use anytime after Session 3.4.

Math Focus Points

◆ Designing patterns for boxes that will hold a given number of cubes

◆ Seeing that the cubes filling a rectangular prism can be decomposed into congruent layers

Materials: student-made boxes for 16 cubes (from Session 3.4), connecting cubes, scissors, tape, M27 (several per pair), R84

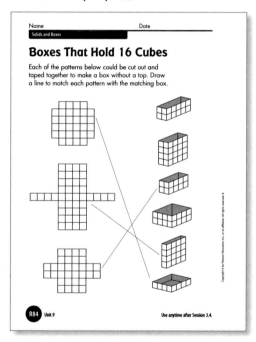

The other day you made patterns to hold 16 cubes. Today you're going to think about these two questions: Are there different rectangular prisms that you can make with 16 cubes? What boxes can you make for those prisms?

Give each pair several copies of Three-Quarter-Inch Grid Paper (M27) and connecting cubes. Pairs work together to find as many different 16-cube rectangular prisms as they can, and to make a box pattern for each possible orientation of that prism. Remind them to refer to the boxes they made in Session 3.4.

Remind students to draw their ideas for patterns on the grid paper, cut them out, fold them, and then fill them with cubes. Patterns that work should be taped together into boxes and saved. Encourage students to use whole sheets of paper when they can. Explain that they may need to tape several sheets of paper together to make some boxes.

You might end by discussing the different rectangular prisms students found (e.g., $1 \times 4 \times 4$, $1 \times 2 \times 8$, $2 \times 2 \times 4$, $1 \times 1 \times 16$), the number of box patterns found for a particular prism, or the variety of types of boxes students made.

Students might say:

"Each box holds 16 cubes. But the number of cubes in the bottom layer is different and the number of layers are different."

Distribute copies of Boxes That Hold 16 Cubes (R84).

ELL English Language Learners

Partner Talk Have ELL pairs describe their boxes. Beginning English Language Learners may only be able to use short phrases. More proficient speakers should be encouraged to use words like *layer, cubes, pattern,* and *rectangular prism* to give more detailed responses.

Additional Resource

Student Math Handbook pages 132–133

Resource Masters

Quiz

Choose the correct answer.

1. Which number has a 5 in the tens place?

    A. 5   **B.** 35   **C.** 52   **D.** 95

2. $29 + 10 =$

    A. 129   **B.** 39   **C.** 30   **D.** 19

3. Which group of coins equals $2.00?

    A. 12 dimes and 10 pennies

    B. 15 dimes and 20 pennies

    C. 17 dimes and 30 pennies

    D. 18 dimes and 50 pennies

4. $100 - 36 =$

    A. 54   **B.** 64   **C.** 74   **D.** 136

5. Show at least 3 combinations of 100s, 10s, and 1s that make 124.

Name   Date

Trading Stickers, Combining Coins

Practicing Adding and Subtracting 10s

Solve the problems below, and show how you got your answers.

1. a. Kenji had 19 stickers. His sister gave him 10 more stickers. How many stickers did he have then?

b. Kenji's brother gave him 20 more stickers. How many does he have now?

2. a. Ines had 67 stickers. She gave 10 stickers to her brother. How many stickers did she have then?

b. Ines gave 20 more stickers to her brother. How many does she have now?

Use anytime after Session 1.2.

More Sticker Combinations

Sheets	Strips	Singles	Equation

On the back of this sheet, explain how you know you found *all* of the combinations of 129 stickers.

Quiz

Choose the correct answer.

1. Which combination makes 100?

A. 30 + 60   **B.** 80 + 20   **C.** 40 + 70   **D.** 50 + 40

2. Which coins make $1.00?

A. 3 quarters, 1 dime   **C.** 6 dimes, 6 nickels

B. 1 half dollar, 2 dimes   **D.** 2 quarters, 5 dimes

3. _____ + 52 = 100

A. 38   **B.** 40   **C.** 48   **D.** 50

4. Which combination makes 158?

A. 15 strips of 10 and 8 singles

B. 158 strips of 10

C. 1 sheet of 100 and 58 strips of 10

D. 15 sheets of 100 and 8 singles

5. Make two 2-digit numbers that have a sum that is as close as possible to 100. Show your work.

| 4 | 5 | 6 | 4 | 3 | 7 |

Trading Stickers, Combining Coins

Making Sums Close to 100

Solve the problems.

1. 3 + _____ = 10

30 + _____ = 100

32 + _____ = 100

2. 1 + _____ = 10

10 + _____ = 100

13 + _____ = 100

3. _____ + 8 = 10

_____ + 80 = 100

_____ + 83 = 100

4. _____ + 5 = 10

_____ + 50 = 100

_____ + 46 = 100

The Dollar Store

The Dollar Store has some toys for sale.
Here are the prices.

car	train	plane	bus
$0.30	$0.10	$0.60	$0.25

Solve the problems, and show your work.

1. Deondra wants to buy a toy plane for her brother. What else can she buy so that she spends exactly $1.00?

_____

2. Benjamin wants to buy 2 toy trains. What else can he buy so that he spends exactly $1.00?

_____

3. Ines wants to buy a toy bus for her collection. What else can she buy so that she spends exactly $1.00?

_____

Quiz

Use the bar graph to choose the correct answer.

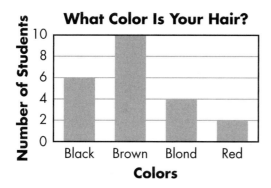

1. How many students have blond hair?

A. 1   **B.** 2   **C.** 4   **D.** 6

2. What color hair do most students have?

A. black   **B.** brown   **C.** blond   **D.** red

3. How many students do **not** have black hair?

A. 16   **B.** 10   **C.** 6   **D.** 3

4. How many students have red or brown hair?

A. 2   **B.** 5   **C.** 10   **D.** 12

5. What are 2 things you can say about this class based on this graph?

More Bar Graphs

Use the bar graph to answer the questions below.

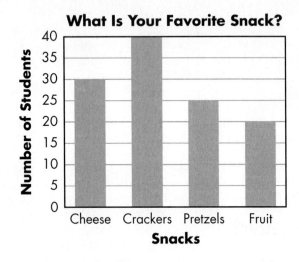

1. How many students participated in the survey? _____
Show how you found your answer.

2. a. Which snack do students favor the most?

_____

b. How many students chose this snack as their favorite?

_____

3. How many students chose cheese as their favorite snack?

_____

Surveys and Line Plots

Data Details

Use the bar graph to answer the questions below.

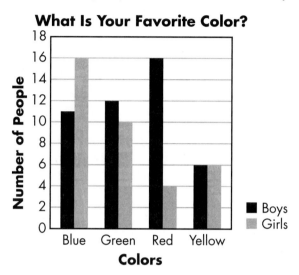

What Is Your Favorite Color?

1. a. Which color is favored by most girls? _____

    b. How many boys favor this color? _____

2. Which color do boys and girls favor the same?

_____

3. What are 2 things that you can say about this group of students based on this graph? Use words such as *half*, *more/less than half*, *very few*, or *almost all* to describe the data.

_____

_____

Quiz

Use the line plot to choose the correct answer.

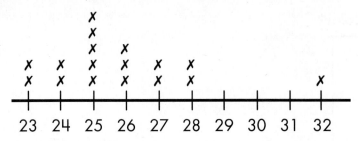

How Many Times I Can Write My Name in 1 Minute

1. How many students wrote their name 27 times?

A. 1 **B.** 2 **C.** 4 **D.** 6

2. What was the greatest number of times a student wrote his or her name?

A. 32 **B.** 31 **C.** 30 **D.** 23

3. How many students wrote their name less than 25 times?

A. 4 **B.** 5 **C.** 9 **D.** 10

4. How many students participated in the survey?

A. 32 **B.** 25 **C.** 23 **D.** 17

5. What are 2 things that you notice about the data?

Representing and Describing Data

The students in Mrs. Dylan's class took a survey about how many times they have visited a museum. Here are their data:

Becky	2	Bridget	1	Cameron	3
Arthur	5	Keith	1	Chris	9
Zhang	4	Dwayne	2	Chiang	5
Gil	2	Elena	2	Murphy	3

1. Use the data to make a line plot.

2. Describe 2 things you notice about the data.

_____

_____

Comparing Two Sets of Data

The students in Ms. Murphy's Grade 3 class took a survey about the number of people who live with them. They collected data from their own class and from Mr. Jackson's Grade 1 class.

Here are the numbers they collected from all of the students. They put the numbers in order.

Grade 1	1, 2, 2, 2, 3, 3, 3, 3, 3, 3, 4, 4, 4, 4, 4, 5, 5, 5, 6, 7
Grade 3	2, 2, 2, 2, 3, 3, 3, 3, 3, 3, 3, 3, 4, 4, 4, 4, 6, 6, 7, 8

1. Represent both groups of data on the same line plot.

2. Write something that is similar about these groups. Write something that is different.

_____

_____

Use anytime after Session 2.4.

Quiz

Choose the correct answer.

1. Dwayne blew his pattern block 1 ruler and 2 more inches. How far did his block go in inches?

    A. 12 inches   **C.** 14 inches

    B. 13 inches   **D.** 21 inches

2. Jane jumped 38 inches. Which describes Jane's jump?

    A. shorter than 3 feet   **C.** longer than 3 feet

    B. exactly 3 feet   **D.** exactly 4 feet

3. Murphy's bedroom is 9 rulers long. How long is Murphy's bedroom?

    A. 9 inches   **C.** 9 yards

    B. 9 feet   **D.** 9 miles

4. Keisha blew a paper clip 2 feet 6 inches. How far did her paper clip go in inches?

    A. 32 inches   **C.** 26 inches

    B. 30 inches   **D.** 24 inches

5. What is 26 inches in feet and inches? Explain how you found your answer.

More Feet and Inches

Complete the table.

Rulers and Inches	Inches	Feet and Inches
2 rulers and 7 more inches		
1 ruler and 11 more inches		
5 rulers and 3 more inches		
4 rulers and 6 more inches		
3 rulers and 7 more inches		
6 rulers and 1 more inch		
1 ruler and 2 more inches		
3 rulers and 3 more inches		
4 rulers and 10 more inches		
5 rulers and 9 more inches		

Use anytime after Session 3.3.

Yards, Feet, and Inches

Solve the problems, and show your work.

1. The desk is 3 feet 11 inches wide. How wide is it in yards, feet, and inches?

2. Justin is 5 feet 1 inch tall. How tall is he in yards, feet, and inches?

3. The path from the window to the door measures 12 feet 8 inches. How long is the path in yards, feet, and inches?

4. The sidewalk from the bus stop to the door measures 22 feet 3 inches. How long is the sidewalk in yards, feet, and inches?

Quiz

Choose the correct answer.

1. How many groups of 10 are in 170?

A. 1 group of 10   **C.** 17 groups of 10

B. 7 groups of 10   **D.** 170 groups of 10

2. Where does 612 go on this number line?

A. to the left of 542

B. between 542 and 588

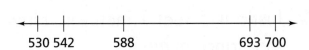

530 542   588   693 700

C. between 588 and 693

D. to the right of 693

3. Which number comes after 283?

A. 291   **B.** 279   **C.** 274   **D.** 192

4. How many 100s are in the sum of 169 + 258?

A. one 100   **C.** three 100s

B. two 100s   **D.** four 100s

5. Show 4 pairs of numbers without using 0 that add to 100.

Addition and the 900 Chart

801				805					
								819	
		844							
					877				
								899	

Solve the problems. Then write the sums on the
900 chart above.

1. 804 + 10 = _____   **2.** 820 + 40 = _____

3. 819 + 30 = _____   **4.** 815 + 20 = _____

5. 844 + 20 = _____   **6.** 802 + 10 = _____

7. 859 + 10 = _____   **8.** 857 + 10 = _____

Collections and Travel Stories

Sequencing Numbers in Four Categories

1. Make a list of 4 different Collection Card categories.

_____   _____

_____   _____

2. Write the 16 numbers in any order.

_____

_____

3. Write the number of items in each collection
in order, starting with the smallest number.

Smallest

____ ____ ____ ____ ____ ____ ____ ____

____ ____ ____ ____ ____ ____ ____ ____

↑
Largest

Use anytime after Session 1.3.

Quiz

Choose the correct answer.

1. 234 + 128 =

A. 262   **B.** 352   **C.** 354   **D.** 362

2. Which number is 40 less than 256?

A. 216   **B.** 252   **C.** 296   **D.** 656

3. 146
  +159

A. 205   **B.** 305   **C.** 306   **D.** 315

4. A fisherman caught 298 fish on Monday. He caught 125 fish on Tuesday. How many fish did he catch in all?

A. 313   **B.** 413   **C.** 422   **D.** 423

5. Ines's first step for solving 124 + 239 was 100 + 200 = 300. Use her first step to solve the problem. Show your work.

Using Addition Strategies

Write an equation to go with the story problem.

1. A restaurant sold 102 salads on Friday.
147 salads were sold on Saturday.
How many salads were sold in all?

Solve each problem, and show your solution.

2. $67 + 99 = $ _____

3. $354 + 26 = $ _____

4. 134
    +228
    ————

5. 271
    + 89
    ————

Use anytime after Session 2.2.

Creating Starter Problems

1. a. Write 3 Starter Problems that could help
you solve 259 + 103 = _____.

b. Solve the final problem, and show your solution.
Circle the starter problem you used to help you.

2. a. Write 3 Starter Problems that could help
you solve 146 + 277 = _____.

b. Solve the final problem, and show your solution.
Circle the starter problem you used to help you.

Quiz

Choose the correct answer.

1. 127 − 59 =

A. 67   **B.** 68   **C.** 78   **D.** 132

2. The difference between 100 and me is 15.
What number can I be?

A. 85   **B.** 90   **C.** 95   **D.** 105

3. Kenji had 53 baseball cards. He gave 15 cards
to his brother. How many cards does Kenji
have now?

A. 68   **B.** 48   **C.** 39   **D.** 38

4. Which equation can you use to find the
difference between 61 and 130?

A. 61 + 130 = _____   **C.** 61 + _____ = 130

B. 130 + _____ = 61   **D.** _____ + 130 = 61

5. Show one way to find the difference
between 81 and 140.

Collections and Travel Stories

"Less Than" Questions

1. What number is 30 less than 194? _____

2. What number is 100 less than 259? _____

3. What number is 50 less than 78? _____

4. What number is 200 less than 315? _____

5. What number is 70 less than 180? _____

6. What number is 120 less than 194? _____

7. What number is 10 less than 95? _____

8. What number is 40 less than 264? _____

9. What number is 300 less than 302? _____

10. What number is 150 less than 166? _____

How Far from 100?

Keisha played *How Far from 100?* with a partner. The 2-digit and 3-digit numbers Keisha used for two rounds are shown below.

Help her fill in the rest of her recording sheet. Then, find the difference between the 2-digit number and the 3-digit number for each round.

Round 1 Cards	Round 2 Cards
_2_ _7_ _4_	_8_ _2_ _6_
How Far from 100?	**How Far from 100?**
Closest 2-digit number	Closest 2-digit number
_7_ _4_ ___	_8_ _6_ ___
Closest 3-digit number	Closest 3-digit number
_1_ _2_ _4_ ___	_1_ _2_ _6_ ___
Score: _____	Score: _____
Difference: _____	Difference: _____

Use anytime after Session 3.5.

Quiz

Choose the correct answer.

1. Ines has 213 stamps in her collection.
Kenji has 174 stamps in his collection.
How many more stamps does Ines have
than Kenji?

   A. 39   **B.** 49   **C.** 61   **D.** 139

2. 196 − 138 =

   A. 162   **B.** 158   **C.** 68   **D.** 58

3. Becky has a packet of 265 flower seeds.
She planted 150 of them. How many are left?

   A. 15   **B.** 115   **C.** 120   **D.** 125

4.   168
    − 59

   A. 119   **B.** 111   **C.** 109   **D.** 9

5. Show one way to solve 237 − 156.

More Subtraction Problems

Write a story problem for each problem, and then solve
the problem.

1. 227 − 73 = _____

_____

_____

_____

2. 153 − 116 = _____

_____

_____

_____

3. 284 − 161 = _____

_____

_____

_____

Use anytime after Session 4.5.

Comparing Heights of Trees

The Nature Center grows a variety of trees and shrubs. The table at the right shows their heights. Use the information in the table to answer the questions.

Kind of Tree	Height in Inches
Bamboo	84
Cherry	223
Forsythia	96
Lilac	115
Azalea	36

1. How much taller is the lilac than the bamboo? Show your work. _____

2. The cherry tree is the tallest. How much taller is it than each of the other trees? Show your work.

_____

Quiz

Choose the correct answer.

1. About how long is the width of a color tile?

    A. 1 inch   **B.** 1 foot   **C.** 1 yard   **D.** 1 meter

2. What is the perimeter of this field?

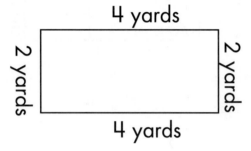

    A. 4 yards   **B.** 6 yards   **C.** 8 yards   **D.** 12 yards

3. What is the perimeter of a square with
    10-centimeter sides?

    A. 10 centimeters   **C.** 40 centimeters

    B. 20 centimeters   **D.** 100 centimeters

4. Which square has the longest perimeter?

    A.   **B.**   **C.**   **D.**

5. The perimeter of a flower garden is 60 feet.
    Draw a picture of what the flower garden
    might look like and label each side.

Perimeter, Angles, and Area

Ordering More Shapes by Perimeter

Use the shapes below to answer the questions.

1. Without measuring, which shape do you think has the longest perimeter? _____

2. Use a centimeter ruler to measure the perimeter of each shape. Put them in order from shortest to longest. Write the perimeter of each shape.

Measurement tool: _____

_____   _____   _____   _____

_____   _____   _____   _____

3. Was your answer to Problem 1 correct? _____

Same Perimeter, Different Shape

Draw 3 different shapes that each have a
perimeter of 24 cm. You may **not** draw
rectangles.

Quiz

Choose the correct answer.

1. What is the area of a 2 by 3 rectangle?

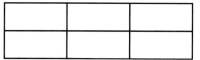

A. 3   **B.** 5   **C.** 6   **D.** 10

2. What is the area of this shape?

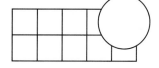

    A. 1 square unit

    B. 2 square units

    C. 4 square units

    D. 5 square units

3. Which square has an area of 16 square units?

    A. 1 by 1   **B.** 3 by 3   **C.** 4 by 4   **D.** 8 by 8

4. What is the area of this rectangle?

    A. 9 square units

    B. 10 square units

    C. 11 square units

    D. 12 square units

5. Make a shape with an area of 8 square units.

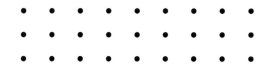

More Perimeter and Area

Find the perimeter and area of this shape.

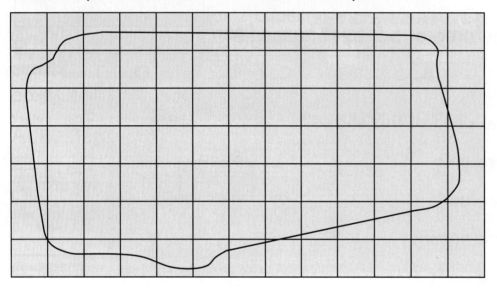

1. Use yarn or string to measure the perimeter of the shape. Describe how you measured the perimeter.

2. What is the area of the shape? Explain how you found your answer.

Another Perfect Cover-Up

1. Try to use as many different types of tetrominoes to cover the square completely. Can you find a way that uses all 5?

Draw the tetromino shapes you used.

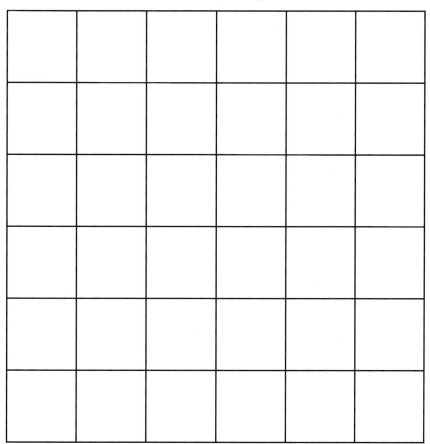

2. What is the area of the square that you covered?

_____

Quiz

Choose the correct answer.

1. Which shape is a triangle?

A.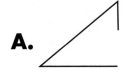

B.

C.

D.

2. How many sides does a parallelogram have?

A. 2   **B.** 4   **C.** 6   **D.** 8

3. Which angle is less than 90 degrees?

A.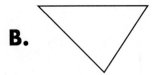

B.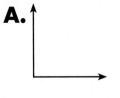

C.

D.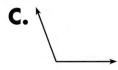

4. How many vertices does a triangle have?

A. 1   **B.** 2   **C.** 3   **D.** 4

5. Draw a quadrilateral that has at least 1 right angle.

Building Shapes

Use your straw building kit.

1. Make a triangle. Draw and label your triangle. Describe your triangle.

2. Make a quadrilateral. Draw and label your quadrilateral. Describe your quadrilateral.

Quadrilaterals with 4 Different Side Lengths

Choose straws of 4 different lengths from your straw building kit. Make as many quadrilaterals as possible using those 4 straws. Draw a picture of each quadrilateral and label the lengths of the sides. Use different lengths than you used in class.

1. How many quadrilaterals did you make? _____

2. Do you think there are more possibilities? Explain your thinking.

Use anytime after Session 3.3.

Name _____   Date _____

Equal Groups

Quiz

Choose the correct answer.

1. $7 \times 2 =$

    A. 9   **B.** 14   **C.** 16   **D.** 21

2. Kim has 3 bags. Each bag has 8 marbles inside. How many marbles are there in all?

    A. 11   **B.** 16   **C.** 22   **D.** 24

3. Which multiplication equation can you use to find $5 + 5 + 5$?

    A. $3 \times 3 = 9$ **C.** $3 \times 5 = 15$

    B. $2 \times 5 = 10$ **D.** $5 \times 5 = 25$

4. Denzel has 5 boxes of crayons. There are 30 crayons in all. The same number of crayons is in each box. How many crayons are in each box?

    A. 6   **B.** 7   **C.** 25   **D.** 35

5. Write a story problem that represents 8×4.

Ears and Toes

Solve the problems and show your solutions.

1. There are 8 people in a group. Each person has 2 ears. How many ears are there in all?

2. There are 6 people in a group. Each person has 5 toes on each foot. How many toes are there in all?

3. Write a story problem about ears that represents 7×2.

Equal Groups

How Many in Larger Groups?

For each problem, write a multiplication equation, solve the problem, and show your solution.

1. In Chiang's picture, there are 8 cartons of eggs. Each carton has 12 eggs. How many eggs are there in all?

2. Murphy drew 9 flowers. Each flower has 8 petals. How many petals are there in all?

3. Elena drew a picture of some stars. Each star has 5 points. There are 55 points in all. How many stars did she draw?

Quiz

Choose the correct answer.

1. Which number is a multiple of 2?

A. 5 **B.** 11 **C.** 19 **D.** 20

2. Which statement is true?

A. The multiples of 10 all end in 5.

B. The multiples of 5 all end in 0 or 2.

C. The multiples of 2 are all even numbers.

D. The multiples of 3 are all odd numbers.

3. Mrs. Jackson's class counted around the class by 6s. What number did the 5th person say?

A. 36 **B.** 33 **C.** 30 **D.** 25

4. If I start at 0 and count by 3s, what number will I **not** land on?

A. 12 **B.** 18 **C.** 27 **D.** 28

5. Write 5 multiples of 10. Explain how you know they are multiples of 10.

Equal Groups

Using Known Multiplication Combinations

Solve the problems. For each problem, write a multiplication equation and show your solution.

1. Beatriz has 3 bunches of balloons. There are 7 balloons in each bunch. How many balloons does Beatriz have?

2. Nicholas has 6 bunches of balloons. There are 7 balloons in each bunch. How many balloons does Nicholas have?

3. Each child has 4 books. How many books do 6 children have?

4. Each child has 8 books. How many books do 6 children have?

Relating Multiples of 3 and 6

Solve these problems and show your solutions. Use a
number line, a 100 chart, or a picture. Use a different
way for each problem.

1. 40th multiple of 3

_____

40th multiple of 6

_____

2. 60th multiple of 6

_____

60th multiple of 3

_____

Use anytime after Session 2.4.

Equal Groups

Quiz

Choose the correct answer.

1. $6 \times 5 =$

   A. 11   **B.** 24   **C.** 25   **D.** 30

2. Which multiplication combination does this array show?

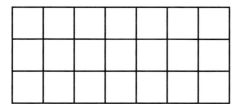

   A. 3×3 **B.** 3×7 **C.** 4×7 **D.** 7×7

3. $4 \times 4 =$

   A. 18   **B.** 16   **C.** 12   **D.** 8

4. How many squares are in this array?

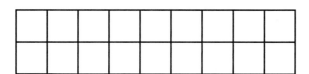

   A. 9   **B.** 10   **C.** 18   **D.** 20

5. Draw 4 arrays for 24. Are there any more possible arrays for 24? Explain how you know.

How Many Petals?

Solve each problem, and show your solution.

1. Draw a flower with 4 petals. How many petals are on 8 flowers like it?

2. Draw a flower with 7 petals. How many petals are on 7 flowers like it?

3. Draw a flower with 9 petals. How many petals are on 4 flowers like it?

Use anytime after Session 3.5.

Equal Groups

Arranging More Chairs

You will need 128 cubes, 5 sheets of Half-Inch Grid Paper, scissors, a glue stick, and 2 sheets of construction paper.

1. Figure out all the ways you can arrange 72 chairs. Draw each rectangle on the grid paper. Cut out each rectangle and glue it onto the colored paper. Label each rectangle with its dimensions. List all your dimensions. Your paper should look like the ones we made in class.

2. Follow the steps in Exercise 1 to find all the ways you can arrange 128 chairs.

Quiz

Choose the correct answer.

1. $24 \div 3 =$

   A. 6   **B.** 7   **C.** 8   **D.** 9

2. Bridget has 15 pennies. She put them into 3 equal piles. How many pennies are in each pile?

   A. 18   **B.** 12   **C.** 6   **D.** 5

3. $6 \times$ _____ $= 42$

   A. 3   **B.** 4   **C.** 6   **D.** 7

4. Zhang paid 45¢ for 5 paper clips. Each paper clip cost the same amount. How much did each paper clip cost?

   A. 10¢   **B.** 9¢   **C.** 8¢   **D.** 5¢

5. Write a story and draw a picture for $12 \div 2$. Then solve the problem and write the answer.

Equal Groups

Finding Factors

Find the missing factors and show your solutions.

1. $2 \times$ _____ $= 14$

2. $25 \div 5 =$ _____

3. $28 \div 4 =$ _____

4. _____ $\times 3 = 27$

5. $6 \times$ _____ $= 36$

6. $24 \div 3 =$ _____

Equal Groups

Problems with Larger Numbers

Solve each problem, and show your solution.

1. Deondra has 5 boxes of crayons. There are 12 crayons in each box. How many crayons are there in all?

2. Cameron has 81 stamps. He will put 9 stamps on each page of his stamp album. How many pages will he use?

3. Four people went to a concert. The tickets cost $11 each. What was the total cost?

4. There are 56 plants in a garden. There are 7 plants in each row. How many rows are there?

Quiz

Use the graph to choose the correct answer.

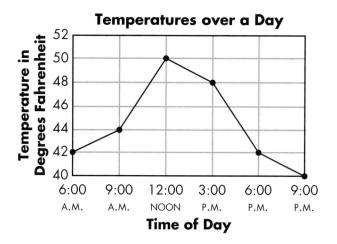

Temperatures over a Day

1. At what time was it the hottest?

   A. 6:00 A.M.   **B.** 9:00 A.M.   **C.** 12:00 NOON   **D.** 9:00 P.M.

2. At what time was it the coldest?

   A. 6:00 A.M.   **B.** 9:00 A.M.   **C.** 12:00 NOON   **D.** 9:00 P.M.

3. How much did the temperature change from 3:00 P.M. to 6:00 P.M.?

   A. 3 degrees   **B.** 6 degrees   **C.** 7 degrees   **D.** 8 degrees

4. At what time was it 44 degrees?

   A. 6:00 A.M.   **B.** 9:00 A.M.   **C.** 3:00 P.M.   **D.** 6:00 P.M.

5. What are 2 things that you see from looking at this graph?

Another Temperature Graph

Use the graph to answer the questions below.

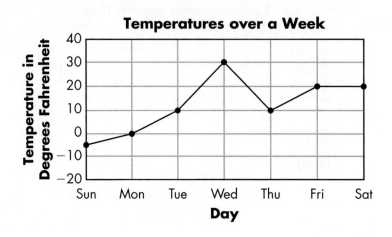

Temperatures over a Week

1. Between which two days does the temperature get cooler?

2. Between which two days does the temperature stay the same?

3. How much did the temperature change from Monday to Tuesday?

4. What is the difference between the highest and lowest temperatures of the week?

What Would You Wear?

Write a story about a place shown on each graph.
Tell what you would wear outside and whether
that is different from what you need at home.
Then name the place.

1. Use the graph on page 1 of the *Student Activity Book.*

Place: _____

2. Use the graph on page 7 of the *Student Activity Book.*
Do **not** use the same place you used in class.

Place: _____

Quiz

Use the cubes to choose the correct answer.

| yellow | black | orange | yellow | black | orange | yellow | black | orange | yellow | black | orange |

1 2 3

1. What is the unit of this pattern?

A. yellow-black-orange   **C.** yellow-orange-black

B. black-yellow-orange   **D.** orange-black-yellow

2. The number 2 is associated with the 1st black cube. What number would be matched with the 8th black cube?

A. 20   **C.** 21

B. 22   **D.** 23

3. The number 1 is matched with the 1st yellow cube. What number would be matched with the 10th yellow cube?

A. 10   **B.** 20   **C.** 28   **D.** 40

4. If the pattern keeps repeating, what is the color of the 60th cube?

A. yellow   **B.** orange   **C.** green   **D.** black

5. If the pattern keeps repeating what is the color of the 100th cube? Explain how you figured it out.

More Repeating Patterns

1   2   3

The number 1 is matched with the 1st star. The number 2 is matched with the 1st moon. The number 3 is matched with the 1st sun.

1. List the numbers for the first 10 suns. What do you notice about these numbers?

2. List the numbers for the first 10 moons. What do you notice about these numbers?

3. List the numbers for the first 10 stars. What do you notice about these numbers?

4. If the pattern continues, what number is the 20th sun? Explain your answer.

5. If the pattern continues, will the 50th figure be a star, moon, or sun? Explain your answer.

Stories, Tables, and Graphs

What Is It?

1   2   3

1. If this pattern keeps repeating, will the 100th figure be a star, a moon, or a sun?

How did you figure this out?

2. If this pattern keeps repeating, will the 200th figure be a star, a moon, or a sun?

How did you figure this out?

3. If this pattern keeps repeating, will the 304th figure be a star, a moon, or a sun?

How did you figure this out?

4. If this pattern keeps repeating, will the 602nd figure be a star, a moon, or a sun?

How did you figure this out?

Quiz

Use the table to choose the correct answer.

Coins Saved

Day	Pilar	Arthur
Beginning	10	12
5	15	22
10	20	32
15	25	42

1. How many coins will Arthur have on Day 20?

    A. 52   **B.** 50   **C.** 46   **D.** 44

2. How many coins will Pilar have on Day 20?

    A. 26   **B.** 30   **C.** 35   **D.** 40

3. Which rule can you use to find the total number of coins for Pilar for any day?

    A. Start with 0. Add 5 for each day.

    B. Start with 5. Add 1 for each day.

    C. Start with 10. Add 1 for each day.

    D. Start with 10. Add 5 for each day.

4. How many coins did Arthur save each day?

    A. 1   **B.** 2   **C.** 5   **D.** 10

5. Compare Pilar and Arthur. What do you notice?

Plotting Points on a Graph

Use the data in the table to make the 2 graphs.
On the back of this sheet, write 3 statements
about what you noticed on the graph.

Cans Collected

Day	Ines	Edwin
Beginning	0	10
5	10	15
10	20	20
15	30	25
20	40	30
25	50	35

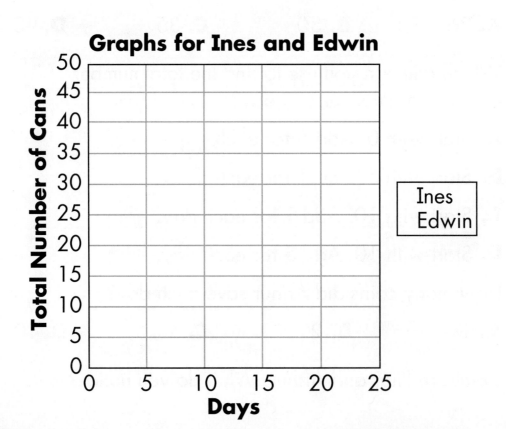

Graphs for Ines and Edwin

Ines
Edwin

Finding a Rule

Suppose you have 19 shells. Imagine you collect 3 shells each day for 30 days. Fill in the table to show how many shells you would have every 5 days. You may use a calculator to help you.

Shells Collected	
Day	**Number of Shells**
Beginning	
5	
10	
15	
20	
25	
30	

1. How many shells would you have on Day 27? Day 50? Explain how you figured it out.

2. On what day would you have 88 shells? 196 shells? Explain how you figured it out.

3. What rule could you use to find the number of shells for any day?

Quiz

Choose the correct answer.

1. How much is $\frac{1}{2}$ of 12 pennies?

    A. 3 pennies   **C.** 6 pennies

    B. 4 pennies   **D.** 24 pennies

2. What part of the square is shaded?

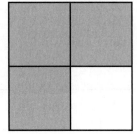

    A. $\frac{1}{4}$ **B.** $\frac{1}{2}$ **C.** $\frac{3}{4}$ **D.** $\frac{4}{3}$

3. Which of the following is equal to 1?

    A. $\frac{1}{2} + \frac{1}{4} + \frac{2}{4}$ **C.** $\frac{1}{4} + \frac{1}{2} + \frac{1}{4}$

    B. $\frac{1}{4} + \frac{1}{4} + \frac{2}{3}$ **D.** $\frac{1}{3} + \frac{1}{3} + \frac{2}{3}$

4. If 3 people share 4 muffins equally, how much will each person get?

    A. $\frac{1}{3}$ muffin   **C.** 1 muffin

    B. $\frac{3}{4}$ muffin   **D.** $1\frac{1}{3}$ muffins

5. Name 2 fractions that are less than $\frac{1}{2}$.
Draw a picture to represent these fractions.

Finding Fair Shares

More Sharing Problems

Write the problems and then solve them. Show
your solutions.

1. Write a story problem that represents $\frac{2}{3}$ of 15 things.

2. Write a story problem that represents 9 things
shared equally among 6 people.

A Sharing Challenge

How can 4 brownies be shared by 6 people?
Draw a picture to show your solution or explain in
words how you solved the problem.

What is each person's share? _____ brownie

Quiz

Choose the correct answer.

1. Which fraction is equivalent to $\frac{1}{3}$?

    A. $\frac{1}{6}$ **B.** $\frac{2}{6}$ **C.** $\frac{2}{4}$ **D.** $\frac{1}{2}$

2. Which combination is equal to 1?

    A. $\frac{2}{4} + \frac{1}{4}$ **B.** $\frac{1}{3} + \frac{1}{6}$ **C.** $\frac{1}{2} + \frac{1}{3}$ **D.** $\frac{3}{6} + \frac{1}{2}$

3. Which combination does **not** make $\frac{1}{2}$?

    A. $\frac{1}{6} + \frac{1}{6} + \frac{1}{6}$ **C.** $\frac{1}{3} + \frac{1}{3}$

    B. $\frac{1}{4} + \frac{1}{4}$ **D.** $\frac{1}{3} + \frac{1}{6}$

4. Which is a true equation?

    A. $\frac{1}{2} + \frac{1}{2} = 1$ **C.** $\frac{1}{4} + \frac{1}{3} = \frac{1}{2}$

    B. $\frac{1}{6} + \frac{1}{6} = \frac{1}{2}$ **D.** $\frac{3}{4} + \frac{1}{2} = 1$

5. Make a design that is half yellow.

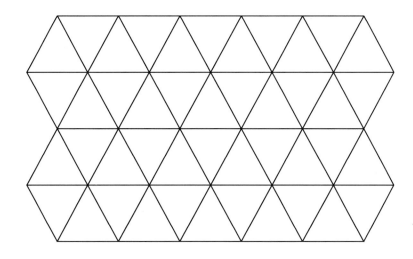

Finding Fair Shares

Is It Half Yellow?

Design 1

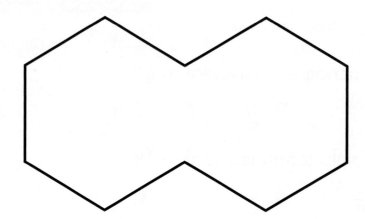

Design 2

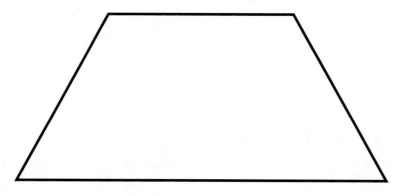

Design 3

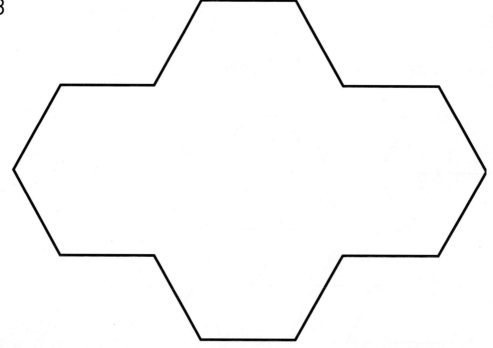

Use anytime after Session 2.4.

Identifying Equivalent Fractions

On the rectangle to the right, shade the equivalent area,
then write the equivalent fractions.

1.

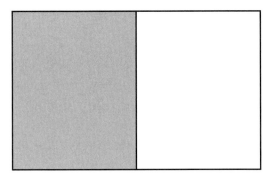   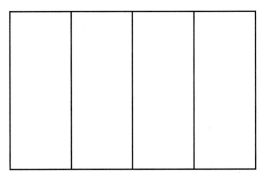

_____ = _____

2.

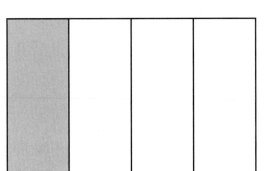   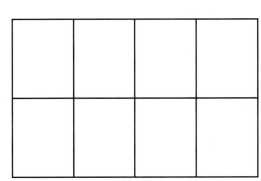

_____ = _____

3.

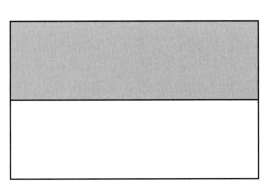   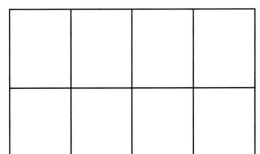

_____ = _____

Quiz

Choose the correct answer.

1. Which fraction equals 0.25?

A. $\frac{1}{4}$ **B.** $\frac{2}{5}$ **C.** $\frac{1}{2}$ **D.** $\frac{4}{1}$

2. Which decimal means $\frac{1}{2}$?

A. 0.1   **B.** 0.2   **C.** 0.5   **D.** 0.75

3. How much is $\frac{3}{4}$ of a dollar?

A. 5 cents   **C.** 50 cents

B. 25 cents   **D.** 75 cents

4. How much would each person get if 2 people shared $5.00 equally?

A. $1.25   **B.** $1.50   **C.** $2.25   **D.** $2.50

5. Make up a problem about equal shares so that each person gets $0.50.

Sharing More Dollars

For each problem, find the share for each person and show how you found it.

1. 8 people share $12.00 equally

2. 10 people share $5.00 equally

3. 12 people share $9.00 equally

My Own Sharing Puzzles

Complete each sharing puzzle. Each fraction is to be
the answer to a sharing puzzle. Then have a friend
show the solution.

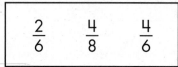

1. If _____ people share _____, how much will
each person get?

2. If _____ people share _____, how much will
each person get?

3. If _____ people share _____, how much will
each person get?

Quiz

Choose the correct answer.

1. 312 + 50 =

    A. 362   **B.** 352   **C.** 350   **D.** 317

2. 7 × 7 =

    A. 14   **B.** 42   **C.** 45   **D.** 49

3. Cameron has 600 paper clips. He used 171 clips to make a display. How many paper clips were left?

    A. 571   **B.** 529   **C.** 439   **D.** 429

4.   400
    − 59
    ———

    A. 459   **B.** 351   **C.** 341   **D.** 241

5. You are playing *Capture from 300 to 600*. Your piece is on 317. Use the cards to make a number that is between 410 and 440. Find as many possible combinations as you can.

    | +5 | +50 | −20 | +40 | +100 |

Addition and Subtraction Practice

Find the solutions. Show your work.

1. $329 + 100 - 20 + 4 =$ _____

2. $597 - 200 - 100 + 10 =$ _____

3. $444 + 40 - 100 + 20 =$ _____

4. $286 + 200 - 30 + 10 =$ _____

5. $411 - 30 + 50 - 20 =$ _____

Extending a Set of Problems

Solve each set of related problems. Then write and solve
2 more problems for each set.

Set 1

300	600	650
− 125	− 125	− 125

Set 2

110	210	210
− 45	− 45	− 125

Set 3

400	800	800
− 70	− 70	− 65

Quiz

Choose the correct answer.

1. 639 + 84 =

   A. 613   **B.** 623   **C.** 713   **D.** 723

2. 176 + 384 + 91 =

   A. 651   **B.** 641   **C.** 551   **D.** 451

3. Elena has a stamp collection. She has
772 U.S. stamps and 299 foreign stamps.
How many stamps does Elena have in all?

   A. 971   **B.** 1,071   **C.** 1,072   **D.** 1,171

4. Which expression is **not** equal to 97 + 123?

   A. 100 + 120   **B.** 90 + 130   **C.** 100 + 123 **D.** 95 + 125

5. Solve the problem. Explain how you found the answer.

$$\begin{array}{r} 880 \\ + \ 375 \\ \hline \end{array}$$

Adding 3-Digit Numbers

Solve each problem in 2 different ways. Show your work.

1. 453 + 377 =	**2.** 674 + 280 =
Start by solving 400 + 300.	Start by solving 674 + 200.
Start by solving 377 + 23.	Start by solving 600 + 200.

Making Equivalent Problems

Solve the problems. Try to make an equivalent
problem for at least one problem in each set.

Set 1

$268 + 374 =$ _____ $397 + 454 =$ _____

Set 2

$149 + 252 =$ _____ $643 + 174 =$ _____

Set 3

$289 + 411 =$ _____ $373 + 166 =$ _____

Use anytime after Session 2.4.

Quiz

Choose the correct answer.

1. 342 − 108 =

A. 234 **B.** 236 **C.** 244 **D.** 246

2. How much greater is 281 than 94?

A. 178 **B.** 187 **C.** 213 **D.** 287

3. Pilar bought a juice box for $1.59. She paid with a 5-dollar bill ($5.00). How much change did she get?

A. $4.41 **B.** $3.51 **C.** $3.41 **D.** $3.31

4. Denzel has 265 stamps in his collection. Arthur has 183 stamps in his collection. How many more stamps does Denzel have than Arthur?

A. 72 **B.** 82 **C.** 122 **D.** 182

5. Write a story for this problem. Then, solve the problem and show your solution.

373 − 128 = _____

Lunch Orders

Item	Price
ham sandwich	$3.18
turkey sandwich	$3.59
juice box	$1.15
bottled water	$0.70
apple	$0.32
banana	$0.39

You have $5.00 to buy a sandwich, a drink, and a piece of fruit. Find 2 different combinations that cost less than $5.00 in all. Then find how much money you have left.

My Lunch Order

List items and prices.

sandwich: _____

drink: _____

fruit: _____

I spent a total of _____.

I have _____ left.

My Lunch Order

List items and prices.

sandwich: _____

drink: _____

fruit: _____

I spent a total of _____.

I have _____ left.

Name _____ Date _____

Subtracting with Larger Numbers

Solve each problem. Show your solutions.

1. $1,488 - 709 =$ _____

2. $1,062 - 511 =$ _____

3. $1,375 - 1,064 =$ _____

4. $2,006 - 1,358 =$ _____

Quiz

Choose the correct answer.

1. Which figure is a pyramid?

A.

C.

B.

D.

2. Which object is shaped like a cylinder?

A. cereal box   **C.** soup can

B. ice-cream cone   **D.** soccer ball

3. Which statement is true?

A. Prisms have points on top.

B. Spheres have 8 vertices.

C. Cones have 12 edges.

D. Cubes have 6 square faces.

4. Which shape rolls?

A.

C.

B.

D.

5. Write the name of a polyhedron. Write at least 2 characteristics of it.

Two Alike, One Different

Pick 2 shapes that are alike in some way.
Color them yellow.

Pick 1 shape that is different. Color it red.

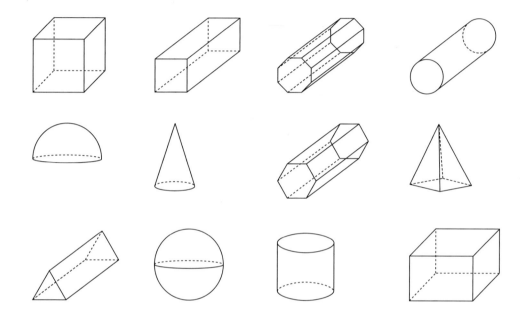

How are the yellow shapes alike?

How is the red shape different from the yellow shapes?

Investigating Pyramids

The number of edges on a pyramid is equal to twice the number of sides of the bottom face.

Complete the table below. Figure out the name for each pyramid. (Hint: The names of some prisms might help you.)

Shape of Bottom Face of Pyramid	Number of Sides on Bottom Face	Number of Edges on Pyramid	Name of Pyramid
1. triangle			
2. square			
3. pentagon			
4. hexagon			
5. octagon			

Quiz

Use the pattern to choose the correct answer.

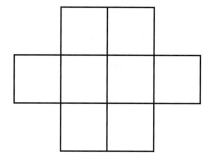

1. If this pattern is folded up to make an open box, how many cubes will fit in it?

   A. 1   **B.** 2   **C.** 3   **D.** 4

2. How will the cubes fit in the box?

   A. 2 cubes will go next to each other.

   B. 1 cube will go on top of another cube.

   C. 3 cubes will go next to each other.

   D. 3 cubes will make a stack.

3. How many cubes across will the open top be?

   A. 6   **B.** 4   **C.** 2   **D.** 1

4. What shape will the base of the box be?

   A. square   **B.** triangle   **C.** cube   **D.** rectangle

5. Use 1-inch grid paper to make a pattern for a 1-cube box.

Patterns for Cube Boxes

Which of these patterns do you think can be used to make an open box for 2 cubes? Write YES next to the letter if you think a pattern will make a 2-cube box. Write NO if you think it will not make a 2-cube box. Cut out the patterns to check your answers.

A _____ B _____ C _____ D _____

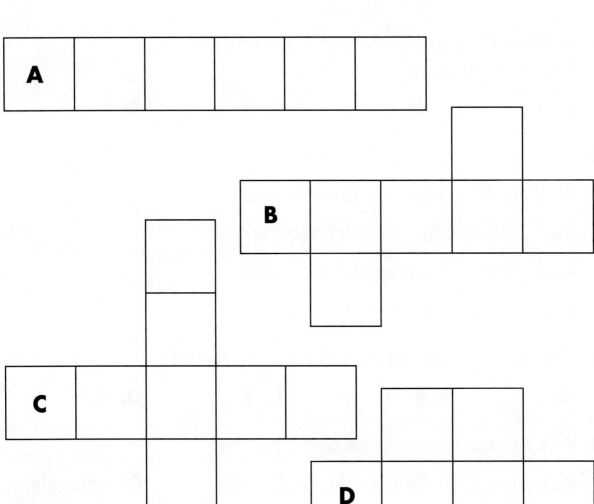

Patterns for 3-Cube Boxes

Which of these patterns do you think can be used
to make an open box for 3 cubes? Write YES next
to the letter if you think a pattern will make a 3-cube
box. Write NO if you think it will not make a 3-cube
box. Cut out the patterns to check your answers.

A _____ B _____ C _____ D _____

Quiz

Choose the correct answer.

1. How many cubes will fill the box made from this pattern?

   A. 4   **C.** 16

   B. 8   **D.** 32

2. How many cubes will fill the box made from this pattern?

   A. 3   **C.** 6

   B. 4   **D.** 12

3. How many cubes will fill the box made from this pattern?

   A. 9   **C.** 2

   B. 5   **D.** 1

4. How many cubes will fill the box made from this pattern?

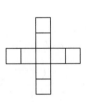

   A. 10   **C.** 18

   B. 12   **D.** 24

5. Circle one of the patterns above and explain how you got your answer.

Use after Session 3.5.

More Box Patterns

Each of the patterns below could be cut out and taped together to make a box without a top. Draw a line to match each pattern with the description of the cubes that would fit in its box.

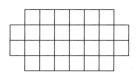

8 cubes in bottom layer
3 layers
24 cubes in all

12 cubes in bottom layer
1 layer
12 cubes in all

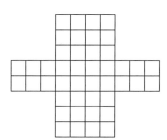

1 cube in bottom layer
4 layers
4 cubes in all

Boxes That Hold 16 Cubes

Each of the patterns below could be cut out and
taped together to make a box without a top. Draw
a line to match each pattern with the matching box.

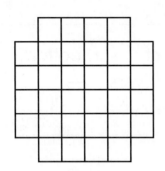

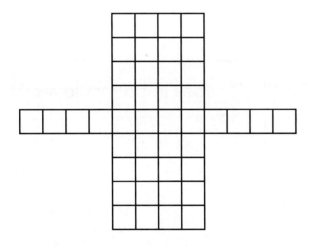

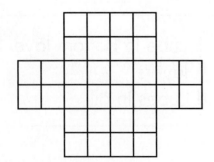

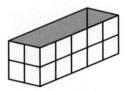

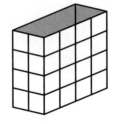

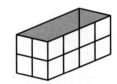

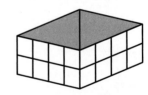

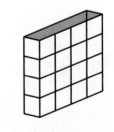

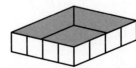